HISTORY ON THE MARCH

ALLAN NEVINS, *General Consultant*

PIONEER
CHILDREN
OF AMERICA

Illustrated by WILLIAM SHARP

By

Caroline D. Emerson

D. C. HEATH AND COMPANY   Boston

Educational Consultant

W. LINWOOD CHASE, Professor of Education,
Boston University

General Consultant

ALLAN NEVINS, Professor of American History,
Columbia University, New York

Copyright © 1959 *by* D. C. Heath *and Company*
Also copyright 1950 *and* 1955

Printed *in the United States of America*   (6 G 3)

Foreword

Sometimes it seems as though grown-up people have more than their fair share of exciting adventures. Especially does this seem true when we read about olden days in America. The grown people like Captain John Smith had the fun of landing in Jamestown. The grown men like Daniel Boone cut a trail west through the forest. They built the first houses. They hunted and trapped animals. They were the ones who had adventures with the Indians.

But really the grown people had only half of the adventures. The country was made by families, and families meant boys and girls. Families were large, and the young people counted for a great deal. The boys and girls had more than their fair share of hard work to do. They had their share of danger and risks. They had their share of excitement.

This book is made up of stories about boys and girls who lived in different places and times in our country. They are exciting stories. But it is important to remember that real boys and girls had just as exciting times. Our country could never have been made as strong as it is today without the help of these boys and girls.

Many famous men started working when they were very young. George Washington was out in the woods and fields when he was thirteen years old. He was learning to measure land. We call the work "surveying." He had to work with great care. He had to add and multiply many figures without a mistake. When he was only sixteen he went on a surveying trip into the wilderness.

There were whole families that went west across our country in covered wagons. That meant crossing deep rivers and hot deserts. It meant walking, walking, walking, for hundreds and hundreds of miles. It meant, perhaps, being killed by Indians.

The boys in pioneer days cut down the forests and burned the brush. They did their share in planting the land and reaping the crops. They took care of the cows and pigs and sheep. They hunted with their fathers. The girls learned to spin and sew and bake. Girls learned to shoot, too. They learned to stand by their fathers and brothers and load the old-fashioned guns when Indians attacked.

It was exciting to be a boy or girl in those days, but it is just as exciting to be young today. In fact it is more exciting. Pedro, who came to Florida in a sailing ship, had never seen a train or an airplane. Molly Harris, the little girl in this book who went over the Wilderness Trail to Kentucky, never saw a city, or an automobile, or a movie. Today boys and girls can see more, hear more, learn more, and do more than in the olden days. Life can be better than it was then, if we make it so.

It is just as important now for young people to be useful as it was then. The more we know the more useful we can be. The more we learn the more we can help make our country a better place in which to live. These stories will tell you about what pioneer children did.

ALLAN NEVINS

Contents

1 First Pioneers

A STORY

OF PIONEER CHILDREN FROM SPAIN

First Pioneers

Pioneers are people who come to a new land to make new homes. Who were the first pioneers to come to this great land of ours?

Indians came first. For more than ten thousand years Indians were the only people living here. Indian children were the first pioneer children in America.

Where did the Indians come from? We do not know. We can only guess. They probably came from Asia. They probably paddled in log or skin boats from one small island to the next. So, little by little, they came to America.

Then, nearly a thousand years ago, the first white men came across the Atlantic Ocean. They found a great land covered with forests. They saw Indians. But they did not stay here. They sailed home.

2

Next came a man from Spain. His name was Columbus. He had three ships, the *Pinta*, the *Niña*, and the *Santa María*. But Columbus did not stay in this new land. He went back to Spain.

At last, white men came who wanted to build homes. In the year 1565, thirty-four ships sailed from Spain. They carried more than two thousand people. They were going to start a town in Florida.

What was it like, crossing the ocean to Florida in 1565? There were no steamships in those days. There were only sailing ships. Wind blew against the sails to push the ships along.

When no wind blew, these ships were helpless. They had no engines. They could not move.

There were no electric lights on the ships. There were no iceboxes. There were not even stoves to cook on.

Today a steamship can cross the Atlantic Ocean in five days. An airplane can fly across in a day.

In 1565 there were no airplanes. There were no telephones. There was no radio. No one knew what might happen when a ship started off. The trip took several months. Sometimes ships were wrecked and never came to shore.

What was it like, crossing the ocean to Florida in 1565? The next story will tell you.

Pedro and Catalina

Chapter 1. LEAVING SPAIN

Pedro jumped to his feet. His eyes shone. What was his father saying? What was going to happen?

But his sister, Catalina, ran to her mother. She hid her face in her mother's lap. She began to sob.

"Don't be afraid," said her mother softly. "We will care for you. There will be other children on the ship."

Pedro's father told them more. The family was to leave Spain. Father, Mother, Pedro, and Catalina were to sail across the sea. They were going to the New World.

4

"Your mother and I have talked and planned for many months," he said.

Pedro was happy and excited. He wanted to start at once. Pedro was nine years old. He could not read or write, but few people could in 1565. He could ride a horse. He owned a sharp hunting knife. It hung from his belt.

Catalina was only seven, but she wore a long, full skirt. She could sew. She was learning to spin. She could sing and dance. Everyone in the village knew and liked her. And now she was to leave that village!

The house was sold. Pans and kettles were packed. The clothes and blankets were folded neatly in the big chest. Mother ran to her garden. She took seeds from the orange and fig trees. She would plant them in her garden in the New World.

"We must not forget anything!" she cried. "There are no stores in the forest. Pedro cannot run back across the ocean for something we forgot!"

At last the family stood on the deck of the ship. They had said good-by to their friends. Mother and Catalina had nearly cried their eyes out, but Pedro was too excited to cry. He wanted to see everything. He almost forgot to help his father.

"Here, son," Father called. "Help me lift this chest."

The harbor was a gay sight that summer day. Many ships were ready to sail. Over two thousand people were starting for Florida. Each ship flew bright silken flags. Sea gulls flew screaming through the blue sky.

"Perhaps we shall find gold in the new land," said Pedro's father. "Perhaps we shall all grow rich."

"More likely we shall all be shipwrecked!" cried his mother. "Perhaps my precious children will be pulled from the water by painted Indians. Perhaps we shall all be slaves!"

Catalina stared at her mother in fear, but Pedro was not afraid. He put his hand to his knife. He was ready for adventure. He wanted to see Indians.

Suddenly a cannon roared. The ship shook. Catalina clapped her hands to her ears, but Pedro liked the noise. Trumpets sounded. Drums beat. The great white sails were raised. A breeze filled them. It smelled of salt.

Pedro shouted. Catalina held her mother's hand tightly. Then something happened. The deck beneath their feet began to rise and fall. The waves were tossing the ship up and down. They had left the still water in the harbor. They were headed for the open sea.

The trip had begun.

Pedro and Catalina watched the houses on shore grow smaller and smaller. Then the fair land of Spain was only a dark line. The blue sea stretched ahead.

"We must find the cabin," said their mother. "Where do we go? What do we do? We must find our things. We must find bunks to sleep on." It all seemed very strange.

She hurried them from the bright sunlight into the dim cabin. It seemed hot and close in there. It was crowded with people and chests. People tumbled over boxes and bumped into each other.

"I wish this ship would stay still," said Catalina.

"It won't do that, not even for the King of Spain himself," laughed a woman.

Pedro unfastened a bundle for his mother. Catalina helped spread blankets on the wooden bunks. Each family had brought its own blankets and dishes. There was little space to put things. People were beginning to complain. Catalina did not like the close air. Her father took her and Pedro out on deck.

The fresh salt breeze made Pedro hungry. M-m-m, the good smell of food! The cook had a great iron kettle hanging over a fire that blazed in a big box of sand on the deck. There were dried peas and salt meat boiling together. Pedro ran back to his mother for bowls. The cook filled one for him and one for Catalina. The hot food tasted good. Afterwards, Mother brought them nuts and raisins. Pedro and Catalina stood by the rail eating. The sun was setting.

There was no clock aboard. Every half hour, a boy turned the sand glass. The sand ran slowly through a little hole. It took just half an hour. Then the glass must be turned over. As the boy turned the glass, he sang out the time for all to hear.

"One glass is gone and now another turneth,
More will run through, if our God willeth!"

The ships rose and fell on the waves. The sun had almost set. It was time for the evening prayer and hymn.

"Listen!" whispered Catalina softly to her mother.

Across the waves came the sound of other voices on the other ships, singing the same hymn. Over a thousand voices joined in the song.

The sun dropped big and red into the water. People started for the cabin. That first night Pedro and Catalina found the wooden bunks hard. They tossed and turned. The two lanterns, with candles burning in them, swung back and forth from the low ceiling of the cabin. They sent strange shadows dancing across the walls.

Just as the children fell asleep at last, they heard the time keeper call out the hour.

"God give us a good night and good sailing!"

Chapter 2. STORM AT SEA

At first the weather was fair. The children played on deck. Pedro found a boy his own age. His name was Martin. Pedro showed Martin his knife. Catalina made a pet of the ship's cat. It had four kittens.

During the day the boys listened to an old sailor who had already been to this new land called Florida. He told them tales of Indians in the strange land.

"They're a great sight, those Indian chiefs," said the old man. "They have tall feathers in their hair and they are painted from head to foot."

12

"Did you ever go hunting with the Indians?" asked the boys eagerly.

"We once watched them hunt alligators," said the old sailor. "Those are beasts worth seeing! They'd snap a man's leg off! The Indians stuck big poles into their mouths and tipped them over. You can shoot an alligator with an arrow through the under side."

Pedro and Martin listened with wide-open eyes. They tried to picture what the new land of Indians and alligators would be like.

In the evening on deck, there was laughter and gay talk. There was singing and dancing. A little dwarf was aboard. He sang and danced well.

"Catalina must dance with him!" said the people. "They are the same size."

At first it was hard for Catalina to dance as the deck rose and fell. But soon her black curls were flying in the breeze. Her eyes were as bright as stars. She whirled about on the deck. People clapped and called for more. Pedro watched his sister proudly.

In nine days the ships reached the Canary Islands. It was good to see trees, and flowers, and fresh fruit again. People were tired of eating dried meat and salt fish. They were weary of the hard sea biscuit that they had to eat instead of bread. They were glad to have fresh water and fruit.

When the ships left the Canary Islands, there was less singing and dancing. People grew quieter. The most dangerous part of the trip lay ahead. The men talked of storms.

One afternoon Pedro and Martin lay on deck looking up at the sky. Suddenly they saw the sun go under a black cloud. The two boys started to their feet. A sudden wind nearly blew them off the deck. They caught hold of a rope and held tightly to it.

The masts of the ship began to rock back and forth across the black sky. Sailors hurried to climb the masts to take in the sails, for such a wind would soon tear the sails to pieces. Pedro and Martin held their breath, as the men climbed the ropes and tugged at the sails. The wind made the sails boom like thunder.

14

The next minute the rain began. The boys ran to the cabin door and hurried inside.

They found everyone busy there. As the ship tossed, boxes and chests began to slide about the floor. They crashed into each other. "A child could be killed by one of them!" cried a woman. People were tying things with strong ropes. The boys rushed to help.

As night came on, the storm grew worse.

"Why did we ever leave Spain?" moaned a woman. "We shall all go to the bottom of the sea and be drowned."

As the ship rocked and tossed, the lanterns hanging in the cabin danced about like crazy things.

Some women wept. Others prayed. Catalina's mother held her in her arms.

"All will be well, if God wills it," she said softly. "We have a strong ship and a brave captain."

It was well they had so fine a man for captain! He was standing and watching each wave, as it rose like a mountain of water before the ship. He ordered the ship steered a little to the left or to the right, so that it might rise safely over each huge wave.

The ship groaned and creaked like a mad thing. Suddenly water began pouring into it.

"Send men to the pumps!" the captain ordered.

There was a leak! Men must pump the water out, or the ship would sink. The men worked as hard as they could. Pedro's father was in charge of the pumps. Pedro and Martin begged to help.

"Stay in the cabin with your mothers!" ordered Pedro's father.

Suddenly there came a deep boom like a cannon. The mainmast had broken. The top of the great pole fell into the sea. The ship gave a roll.

"The ship is sinking!" a woman screamed.

But this time the ship righted itself. Catalina buried her head in her mother's arms.

16

Chapter 3. PEDRO'S KNIFE

Waves broke across the deck in a mass of green water and white foam. They pounded against the cabin door. Then a giant wave struck. There was a crashing sound. Suddenly the great door of the cabin swung wide open. The bolt on the heavy door was broken. Water poured in. Wind and rain swept through the cabin.

"Quick, Pedro, quick!" cried his mother. "Close that door."

Martin was near, and the two boys jumped to their feet. A roll of the ship sent them tumbling to the floor. Pedro's head hit a sharp corner of a chest. He saw stars. For a minute he lay there. Then cold sea water splashed over him and brought him to his senses.

The two boys crawled to the door. It was swinging wildly back and forth, as the ship rocked. Together they pushed the door shut. They tried to hold it shut, but the wind slammed it open again and knocked them down. Water washed about them. Up they jumped again and pushed the door.

"If only we could fasten it shut," panted Martin. "If only we had a strong nail to drive through the broken bolt."

Pedro thought of his knife. He reached to the case at his side. He pulled out his precious knife. He pushed it through the hole in the broken bolt.

"Give me something to pound it in with!" he cried. "Quick! Quick! We must drive it into the wood."

Martin pulled a small iron kettle loose from the rope that held it. The boys used it to pound the knife through the bolt and into the wood. They drove the blade deep into the wood of the doorpost. Then they stood back against the wall, panting. The bolt held. The door stayed shut!

Pedro crept back to his mother. His head was bleeding. His mother wiped his face and tucked a blanket around him. He was glad to lie still.

18

All the long black night the storm tossed the ship about. But by morning the rain stopped. The wind was not quite so fierce. People looked at one another. They dared to hope that they were safe.

A sailor who had come up from below pulled at the heavy cabin door to open it. He could not get Pedro's knife loose, so he broke it in half with a hammer. Pedro looked at it sadly.

Then Pedro and Martin crept out on deck. The fresh air smelled good. The boys looked out over the rough sea.

"Where are the other ships?" cried Pedro. There was not one in sight.

For many days the seas were rough. People were sick and miserable. The sea biscuit was wet. The dried meat and salt fish began to spoil. The drinking water was so stale that Catalina could hardly swallow it.

But at last land was sighted! At last the ship sailed into harbor. People hurried out on deck. The ship had reached the island of Puerto Rico. People from Spain had already built a town there.

"It is good to see houses and trees and dry earth again!" cried Catalina's mother.

Some of the ships were already in the harbor. People shouted to each other. They waved and called eagerly to friends.

But where were the other ships? Were they wrecked in the storm? Did they turn back to Spain? No one could say. Many a ship was lost in those days and never seen again.

The ships' carpenters worked hard before the ships set out again. There were many repairs to be made after the storm. But at last the ships were ready to sail away. Florida lay ahead!

Time passed quickly. The sun shone. The women opened the chests and dried out the clothes that had been wet with salt water.

"My best red dress!" sighed one woman. "I can never wear it again."

But the ship was safe. Florida was near. People were eager and excited. Suddenly one night a comet flashed across the sky.

"It is for good luck!" the people said.

It was two months since the ships had left Spain.
At last Florida came in sight. Pedro and Martin saw
the low sandy shore. They looked for Indians and
alligators, but all they saw were palms and palmettos,
live oak and pine trees.

The general in charge of all these ships was named
Menéndez. At last, he chose the place to land.

The cannon on the ships roared. Drums beat and
trumpets sounded as Menéndez stepped ashore. He
wore a shining suit of armor and a velvet cape. He
carried the great gold and red flag of Spain.

The boys watched as General Menéndez knelt and claimed the land for Spain.

"Look!" whispered Pedro suddenly to Martin. "Indians!"

A group of red warriors had slipped quietly from the deep woods to watch the strange new white men who had landed on their shores.

Later, as Pedro left the cabin of the ship, he looked sadly at his knife. The bolt on the door had been mended, but part of the knife was left sticking into the wood. The handle had been broken off. The blade was bent. Pedro put his hand on it. The precious knife! How he wished he had it back!

Just then Pedro heard a sound behind him. It was his father. He laid his hand on Pedro's arm.

"You did well, son," he said. "Your mother told me of the night of the storm. She told me how you and Martin fought to keep the door shut. If the cabin had flooded with water, the ship might have sunk. You did well. Here is another knife to take ashore with you. It is a finer one."

He drew out his own knife and slipped it into Pedro's empty case. Pedro cried out his thanks. Then he followed his father out on deck. He was ready to land on this strange shore.

22

So the people from Spain came to Florida in the year 1565. They started a town which they called St. Augustine because land was sighted on that saint's day. They built a fort.

Today a fort stands near where that old fort stood. Today St. Augustine is a busy American city by the sea. Each year many people from all parts of the country go there to visit it.

It is the oldest city on the mainland of the United States.

1.

The first Spanish people who came to this country had far bigger boats than the Indians. This is how a ship looked.

2.

Sailing ships usually had three masts. The tallest mast was the mainmast. The straightest trees were saved for masts.

3.

The ships had big canvas sails. The bars that held them were called yards. Sailors climbed along the yards to take in sails.

4.

It was hard and dangerous work to take in the sails in a storm. Sometimes sailors fell overboard.

5.

Sometimes in a storm a ship began to leak. Then men had to pump out the water. If the ship filled with water, it would sink. Men pumped night and day.

6.

On pleasant days a sailing ship was a fine place to be. A fresh breeze blew. The ship flew over the waves. The sailors sat on deck and fished.

7.

Food was cooked on deck in a big iron kettle. A fire was made in a box of sand. Enough wood for the whole trip had been brought along.

8.

The inside of the ship looked like this. There were hard wooden bunks in the cabin. Food and water were stored in the hold below the cabins.

Things to Talk About

1. What is a pioneer?
2. Tell experiences that you have had with boats.
   Make a list on the blackboard of the different kinds of boats that you have seen.
   Which go the fastest and farthest? Why?
3. How was the ship that Pedro and Catalina came in different from our big steamships today?
4. Who are the people in this story? Ask your teacher to write their names on the blackboard. Tell something about each one.
5. What is a comet?

Things to Do

1. Draw a picture of a ship like the one that brought Pedro and Catalina to America.
2. Bring in pictures of all kinds of ships. Put up an exhibit on the bulletin board. Have an exhibit of ship models and toy boats.
3. These sentences tell what happened in the story. They are not in the right order. Which sentence tells what happened first? Which tells what happened next? Read the sentences in the right order.
   a. Pedro and Catalina reached Florida at last.
   b. The cabin door blew open and water poured in.
   c. Pedro and Catalina sailed away from Spain.
   d. Pedro and Martin pounded the knife into the doorpost to hold the broken bolt.

26

4. Bring an egg timer to school if you have one at home. See how long it takes for the sand to run through. Is the egg timer anything like an hour glass?

5. Which of the sentences below make you think of a storm at sea?
   a. The waves were like mountains.
   b. The sails boomed like thunder.
   c. The Indians hunted alligators.
   d. The ship groaned and creaked like a mad thing.
   e. People sat on deck in the sun and fished.

Things to Find Out

1. Some words are two words. The short words often tell what the long word means. Explain these words.

   shipwreck   mainland   doorpost   steamship

2. The word *roll* has three different meanings.
   a. To move along by turning over and over
   b. A kind of bread
   c. Something that is rolled up, like a roll of paper.

   Which of these three meanings is used in this sentence?

   "The feather bed was tied into a roll."

3. How many meanings can you think of for these words?

   waves   chest   yard   pound   trip

4. St. Augustine is the oldest city on the mainland of our country. The very oldest city in our country is on the island of Puerto Rico. See if you can find these places on the map.

   Spain   Puerto Rico   Florida

27

2 English Pioneers

A STORY OF PIONEERS IN VIRGINIA

English Pioneers

In the year 1607 three small ships brought pioneers from England. They sailed up the James River and they started a little town called Jamestown. It was named for King James of England.

It was hard work building homes in this new land. Many men had come to Jamestown hoping to find gold. They hoped to grow rich. Instead, they found hard work.

Many men grumbled. Many were hungry and sick. Then one man took charge. He was called Captain John Smith. He said that anyone who did not work should not eat. After that more work was done.

Trees were chopped down. A few poor huts were made. A fort was built. A wall was built around the little town. It was needed, for many of the Indians did not want the white men to come to this land.

Captain John Smith went often to the Indian villages. He bought corn from the Indians to keep the white men from starving. The English people had never seen Indian corn before. They learned to use the Indian corn for corn bread. They learned to plant it in the little fields outside the wall of the town. Corn became their most important food.

Captain John Smith did all that he could to keep peace with the Indians. But other Englishmen were not so wise as he. Often there was trouble with the Indians. People felt safer to have a fort with guns on it. People felt safer to have a wall around the town with a great gate to shut at night.

At first there were only men in Jamestown. But soon mothers and children came across the water from England. It was hard for the mothers to make their families comfortable in this new, strange land. There were no stores to sell what was needed. A few things were brought from England. The people must make the rest for themselves.

What was it like, living in Jamestown in those early days? The next story, "The Runaway," will tell you.

The Runaway

Chapter 1. SALLY AND DICK

Eight-year-old Sally sat in the doorway knitting. Knit, knit, knit! Was there ever an end to it?

There were two brothers to knit stockings for. Sally's fingers were never still. She must work all summer to be ready for winter.

In winter, feet were often cold and wet. There were no rubbers or overshoes in those days. There were no hard, dry sidewalks. In Jamestown there were only dirt paths and they were often muddy. Warm knitted stockings were a comfort to cold feet in wet shoes.

Knit, knit, knit! Sally's fingers flew.

"Sally!" called her mother. "Watch the kettle that is hanging over the fire. Don't let the dinner burn. And mind the baby. I'm taking the clothes to the river to wash."

It was easier to carry the wash to the river than to pull bucket after bucket of water from the well. The goodwife picked up a big bundle. The mother of a family was called "goodwife" in those days, and a good wife she needed to be with all the work there was to do. The goodwife took a gourd filled with soft soap from the shelf.

Sally had helped her mother make that soap. It had been hard, hot work. They had saved grease and fats. Wood ashes had been saved from the fireplace. The ashes were put in a barrel and water was poured through. That made the lye. When the lye was ready, the fat was boiled in a big soap kettle. Then the lye was put in. Lye was magic, Sally thought. Lye turned fat into clean soap.

Off to the river went the goodwife with her bundle of clothes on her head, and her gourd of homemade soap in her hand. She was a good housekeeper. There was no better one in all Jamestown. Her linen was always white and clean. Her fire always burned in the fireplace.

That fire! Two years it had been burning. Never once had it gone out, day or night. Each evening the goodwife covered the red coals with ashes. Every morning she blew on the red coals and fed them little bits of dry sticks till the fire blazed up. Never once had her fire gone out.

Sometimes neighbors were careless. Sometimes they let their fires go out at night. Then they came running to the goodwife. They borrowed red coals to light their fires. There were no matches in Jamestown. No one had ever heard of matches in those days.

Sally went to the fire now, and peeked into the big iron kettle that was hanging in the fireplace. The deer meat smelled good. She put more wood on the fire. Then back she went to her knitting.

Small Dick played on the floor with some shells. He was only three. No small boy today would wear the clothes Dick wore. He had on a long skirt. Boys in those days did not wear pants until they were six or seven years old.

As Dick stood up, he stepped on his skirt. There was a loud tearing sound.

34

"Oh, dear," sighed Sally. "Another patch! There is more patch than dress now!"

It was hard to get cloth in this new land. Eight-year-old Sally knew how to mend and patch as well as knit.

Dick was pointing to a box on a shelf.

"No, no, Dick! You can't have it," said Sally firmly.

Sally longed to peek into the box herself. Brother Ralph had brought home a baby squirrel. He had caught the tiny thing in the forest. He was taming it.

Ralph had made the box from pieces of wood. Sally had watched the squirrel curl up in it to sleep. The little animal had spread out its fluffy tail for a covering. Sally had laughed with delight.

Now Dick wanted to play with the squirrel. It was lucky that the shelf was high. Sally gave Dick a bit of cold corn bread. For a while he forgot the box. He ate the bread eagerly. He was hungry.

"The boys always seem to be hungry," sighed Sally. She was often hungry herself. Sometimes she sat and thought about good things to eat.

There was not much food in the house. Last year's corn was nearly gone. This year's corn was not yet ripe. In the morning the children ate their hot corn meal and scraped the wooden bowls clean. They did not ask for more. They knew better.

But the men had shot a deer yesterday. There would be deer meat for dinner even though there was not much else. It smelled good as it cooked over the fire.

Dick grew sleepy. Sally put him in the old wooden cradle. Father had made that cradle. She rocked and sang as she knitted. Soon Dick's eyes closed.

Then Sally heard her mother calling. The goodwife wished help in spreading the linen on the ground to whiten in the sun. Oh, there were so many napkins to spread out! For there were no forks in Jamestown. People did not use forks in those days. There were spoons and knives, but people ate their meat in their fingers. Plenty of napkins were needed.

"Sally!" called the goodwife. "Come and help me."

36

Sally ran out into the sunlight. It looked as though it had been snowing, so much white linen lay on the ground.

The goodwife was famous for her linen. She had spun the thread and woven it. She had brought a big chest of it with her from England. There might not be much to eat on her rough wooden table. There might not be much food, but there were fresh napkins.

While Sally worked, something was happening inside the house.

Chapter 2. OUTSIDE THE GATE

While Sally was away, something happened!

A fly tickled Dick's face. There were no screens to keep flies out. Dick woke up. There was no one there. He sat up and looked about.

He saw the box on the shelf. The squirrel was inside. Dick rubbed his eyes. Then he climbed out of the cradle.

There was the big chest against the wall. Dick climbed onto it. He stood on tiptoe. He could just reach the shelf. Little by little he pushed the box toward the edge.

The box fell. There was a crash. The top flew off. Out jumped the tiny animal. It ran about the room. Dick nearly fell off the chest as he tried to catch it.

The squirrel sat up and scolded him. Then it ran out the open door into the sunshine. Dick hurried after it.

When Sally came back, she found the room empty. She saw the box on the floor. There was no Dick asleep in the cradle. There was no sign of Dick in the little house.

Sally ran outdoors looking and calling. She ran to the neighbors, but no one had seen the runaway. Her mother had gone back to the river. She was out of sight.

Then Sally saw marks of small bare feet in the path. The marks led toward the gate in the wall that protected the town. Sally ran toward it. There was no guard at the gate. The men were all working in the fields outside the wall. No one had seen the runaway.

Sally's heart beat fast. Where was Dick? What had happened to him? Sally stopped at the gate. Beyond the fields was the forest. In the forest the trees were tall and dark. The forest was full of flowers and birds and sweet wild strawberries. But there were Indians and wild animals, too! The men always carried guns when they went into the woods.

For a moment Sally stopped. Then she saw the marks of Dick's small bare feet. She followed them out the gate as fast as she could go. They led across a small corn field. Then they went into the forest.

On and on Sally ran, following the tracks. Bushes caught her dress and tore it. There were ugly red scratches on her arms and legs. Then a vine tripped her up.

"Dick! Dick!" she called. "Where are you, Dick?"

Just then she heard an answer. There was a clearing in the woods ahead. She peered around the big trunk of a tree.

There was that rascal! There was Dick! He was sitting on a grassy spot eating wild strawberries. His face and hands were red.

Sally threw herself down on the grass beside him. She was hot and tired. Then she saw the berries. They looked like little glowing red coals. She, too, began to eat. They were sweet and juicy.

40

Suddenly Sally remembered that they were far from home, and alone.

"We must get home, Dick," she cried.

She pulled Dick to his feet. They started back. But which way should they go? For a minute Sally's heart stood still. Then she heard sounds. Guns were being fired. There were shouts and cries.

It was easy now to tell which way to go. Sally started toward the sound of the guns. She dragged Dick after her. He was tired and scratched and crying.

Another gun was fired. What was happening?

"Hurry, Dick! Hurry!" cried Sally. "Something has happened!"

Perhaps Indians were attacking the fort. She must get Dick inside the wall. Perhaps the gate would be closed when they reached it. No one knew that they were outside. Sally half carried the tired Dick.

At last she saw the gate ahead. It was still open. Sally ran through it and pulled Dick after her. Then she stopped for a minute to get her breath.

People were running through the little town with buckets in their hands. The men had rushed back from the fields at the sound of the gun. Now they were carrying buckets of water from the river.

Sally saw that smoke was pouring from the door of her home.

Chapter 3. FRIENDS IN NEED

There were no fire engines in those days. There were no fire hose and pumps. The men stood in a line from the river to the house. They passed buckets of water from one man to the next as fast as they could.

Sparks had flown out from the fireplace in Sally's house. One spark had landed in Dick's cradle. The soft wool blanket had blazed up. Soon the wooden cradle was in flames. Then the wall started to burn. Wooden houses burned easily! Luckily a neighbor had seen the smoke. She had run for help. Ralph had fired a gun to call his father and the men from the fields.

Water was dashed on the flames. Bucketful after bucketful was thrown on. At last there was only smoke.

Sally followed her father into the kitchen. Tears ran down her face from the smoke and the smell of burning wool. But the fire was out. The house was saved.

Then everyone began to talk at once. It was sad that the blanket was burned. It was too bad that the cradle was gone. The wall would have to be patched a little. That was all the harm done. It was lucky that the house had been saved!

"It was my fault! It was all my fault!" cried the goodwife when she heard Sally's story. "I never should have called Sally to help me. I should not have called her away. This would never have happened if I had not called her away."

She hugged Sally and Dick in her arms. But just then Sally looked toward the kettle.

43

"What will we eat for dinner?" she cried.

The deer meat was burned to coals. There was nothing in the kettle but black coals. What were they going to eat? What were they going to do?

There were no iceboxes to go to in those days. There were no cans to open. There were no stores to run to. But, luckily, there were good neighbors. They did not have much themselves, but they shared what they had.

A little of this and a little of that was put on the bare wooden table. It is often so. Those who have least, share most. They know what it is like to have children go hungry to bed.

At last the family sat down to dinner. Father sat at the head of the table in the big chair that had come from England. The rest of the family sat on three-legged wooden stools that Father had made from logs.

Before they ate, Father bowed his head in prayer. He gave a prayer of thanks.

"Oh," thought Sally, "there is so much to be thankful for!"

She was thankful that Dick was safe. She was thankful that the house had not burned down. She was thankful that the neighbors had given them something to eat. She was very hungry.

44

Suddenly there was a little sound at the window. Everyone looked that way. A tiny nose peeked in. Two very bright eyes looked at them.

"It's the baby squirrel!" cried Sally. "It's come back!"

The tiny thing ran to Ralph. It cuddled down inside his jacket. It was lonely. It had missed him.

"That's something else to be thankful for," said Sally.

That evening the family sat around the open fire as usual. The goodwife was busy mending. Sally knitted as fast as she could. Ralph worked with his knife. He was cutting out a wooden mixing bowl for his mother, from a piece of oak wood. Dick sat on his father's lap.

As they worked of an evening, their father often told stories of the old days.

Sometimes he told of the trip across the ocean from England. Sometimes he told of the first hard winters in Jamestown.

This evening Sally asked for the story that she liked best. It was about the little Indian princess, Pocahontas, who had saved the life of Captain John Smith.

Pocahontas had been brought up in the forest. She was the daughter of a great Indian chief. Once the chief had captured Captain John Smith. He ordered one of his warriors to kill the white man. But Pocahontas had thrown herself between the warrior and the white man. She had begged her father to save the man's life. Her father had looked at her in surprise. Then he had given the sign. The warrior stepped back. Captain John Smith was saved.

Sally had often seen Pocahontas in Jamestown. Pocahontas was a graceful, slender little Indian maid. She had often helped the white people. She had brought them corn when they were starving. She had warned them of Indian attacks.

Of all the stories that her father told, Sally liked best the story of Pocahontas.

46

At last Sally's head began to nod. Dick was sound asleep in his father's arms. His cradle was burned, but he could sleep with Sally in her bed in the corner of the kitchen.

Sally felt herself lifted up in her father's strong arms. She was carried across the room. Her mother slipped off Sally's clothes. Soon she and Dick were tucked safely in the little bed.

Ralph climbed to the loft where he slept. He carried his squirrel with him. The goodwife covered her red coals carefully so that the fire would keep for the night. Soon all was dark and quiet in the little house in Jamestown.

HOW SOAP WAS MADE

1.

2.

Soap making was hard, hot work! Everyone dreaded the day. Scraps of fat and grease from cooking were saved in a big iron kettle.

All winter, wood ashes were saved in a barrel. Water was poured in. It soaked slowly through the ashes and made lye.

3.

4.

The lye had to be strong to make good soap. When an egg would float in the lye, it was strong enough. Only a little of the egg should show.

A fire was built under the big kettle outdoors. The boys chopped the wood. Smoke got in everyone's eyes. Everyone hated the smell of hot fat.

5.

The lye was poured carefully into the hot fat. Lye burns. It must not splash on hands or clothes. Be careful!

6.

The lye was stirred with a long wooden spoon. If it was just the right strength, it turned the grease into soap.

7.

The top of the soap was hard enough to cut into cakes. The rest was put into a soft-soap barrel. It was dipped out with a gourd.

8.

At the end of the day, everyone was tired out. But there was soap enough on hand to last a long time. People were careful not to waste it.

Things to Talk About

1. Name three things that the pioneers made at home that we buy in stores. Have you some things at home that were made there? People are proud of things that they have made themselves.

2. Why did the people at Jamestown build a wall around their town? What was it made of?

3. From what country did the people in Jamestown come? Where did the people who settled in St. Augustine come from?

4. Tell how Sally helped her mother make soap.

5. What did you eat for breakfast? What did you have that the first settlers in Jamestown did not have? Why can we have more things today than they had?

6. Look at pages 45 and 47. What is happening in the pictures?

Things to Do

1. Bring a gourd to school if you can. How did the pioneers use gourds?

2. Bring an ear of corn to school if you can. Learn the names of the different parts of the corn:

   husk   stalk   silk   ear   kernel

   Pound some of the kernels to make corn meal. Plant some in a flowerpot. Keep the pot in the sunshine.

3. Fire was hard to make before the days of matches. Get a boy scout to show you a way to make fire without matches.

50

4. If some members of the class can knit, ask them to bring their knitting to school. What can you see in the room that is knitted?

5. Make pages for a class scrapbook called "How the Pioneers Lived."

   After you have read each story in the book, make drawings to paste in the scrapbook. Make drawings of things that you read about in each story, such as a gun, a bucket, and a cradle. Write the name under each picture.

6. Act out something that happened in the story. Let the class guess which scene it is.

Things to Find Out

1. Some of the words below tell about Sally. Some of the words tell about Dick. On one side of a piece of paper write the name *Sally*. On the other side write *Dick*. Then copy the words that tell about each person under the right name.

a rascal	a help to Mother	a runaway
three years old	knitted stockings	slept in a cradle
helped make soap	eight years old	chased a squirrel

2. Read page 44. Tell three things that Sally was thankful for.

3. Read page 45. What were the different members of the family doing as they sat by the fire in the evening?

3 Pilgrim Pioneers from England

A STORY OF PIONEERS IN PLYMOUTH

Pilgrim Pioneers from England

Other pioneers who came from England were the Pilgrims. The Pilgrims did not come to find gold. They came to find a place where they could live in peace. They wished to have their own church. In England, they could not live as they wished.

In 1620 the Pilgrims came to this country in a ship named the *Mayflower*. It was a small ship, but it carried over a hundred people. A new baby boy was born on the way.

The Pilgrims landed at Plymouth. It was near Christmas day when the Pilgrims came ashore, but there was no giving of Christmas presents. The Pilgrims were a serious people. They did not believe in making merry.

54

The men started to cut down trees, but they were not Christmas trees. One big house for all to share must be built, and built quickly. Everyone who could work must help.

The Pilgrims did not build log cabins. It would have been better if they had. Log cabins were easier to make than board houses. They were warmer. But the Pilgrims did not know how to make log cabins.

They split and sawed logs into beams and boards. They fastened the beams together with wooden pegs. They had brought a few nails with them, but nails were hard to get. Each nail had to be made by hand.

What was it like, building the first house in Plymouth? There were no cement mixers or steel beams. There were no brickyards to bake clay into red bricks. There were no lumber yards where the Pilgrims could buy smooth, sweet-smelling boards. There were no stores where one could get nails and locks. There were no doors, or window frames, or window glass to be had.

But there were tall trees. There were men with strong hands and arms. They had brought axes and saws from England. They had also brought sharp iron wedges to split logs into planks.

What was it like, building the first house in Plymouth? The next story will tell you.

House Raising

Chapter 1. IN THE FOREST

"Do you think we will see Indians?" asked Thomas.

"The less we see of Indians the better!" said a man. "The other day an arrow missed my hat by an inch!"

Thomas followed his father and several other men toward the forest. It was a chill, damp day. The bare trees were black against the gray winter sky.

The boy looked back at the *Mayflower*. The ship looked small and lonely as she lay in the harbor. He was tired of being shut up in that ship! He was glad to be ashore at last. The men had been ashore before, searching and hunting for a good place to build homes. The women and children had been left on board.

There were only a few trees near the shore where they landed. Back from the shore was a wooded hill. Thomas followed the men to the woods. He peered between the great trunks of the trees. He was excited, and still he was afraid. What was in those woods?

Something moved beside him. Thomas gave a cry. The men came running with their guns.

"What is it?" they shouted. "What do you see? Indians?"

A slow porcupine walked heavily across the dead leaves. The men began to laugh.

But one man said crossly, "Keep your cries to yourself, lad! You've no business to frighten us. Use your head, or stay with the women on board the ship!"

Thomas turned red. He had not meant to cry out.

The men soon forgot him. They chose strong oak trees to cut. Thirty or forty trees would be needed for the house. Soon the woods were filled with the sounds of chopping.

Those woods had never heard such sounds before! Frightened deer ran swiftly away. A bear turned over in his winter bed. Was a storm blowing the trees down? Squirrels scolded the strangers for spoiling their winter homes.

"Count my strokes, lad," said Thomas's father. "They say ten strokes of an ax should bring down a fair-sized tree."

Chips flew. The smell of fresh-cut wood filled the air. But ten strokes did not bring down the tree. Thomas counted ten and then ten more.

His father stopped to rest. His hands were sore.

"Let me try," begged Thomas.

He was eager to help. He gripped the ax as he had seen his father do. He tried to give the tree a heavy blow. Instead, he hardly hit the tree. He dropped the ax. He tipped himself over. He fell onto the ground.

"The boy's not big enough for an ax," said one of the men. "He will cut his foot open the next thing you know. He should be back with the women and children."

Thomas bit his lip. He wanted to help. But everything he did was wrong.

"Look out!" someone shouted. "The first tree is coming down!"

A tall proud tree began to tip. There was a crashing of branches. The tree fell faster and faster until it struck the ground. Then the tree lay still.

It was a great sight to see that big tree lying low. It had been so tall and beautiful. Now it lay so helpless. The men walked along the broad trunk. They cut off branches with their axes. Here was a place a boy could help.

"Take this hatchet and cut the smaller branches into firewood," called his father. "But watch out, son. Don't cut yourself. Think what you're doing. Use your head."

Thomas worked away. The wind was chill and damp, but he was soon warm from the work. He piled his wood, ready to carry to the ship.

The men sawed the trunk of the tree to the right length for a great beam. Then they cut the sides square with their axes. At last the first beam for the new house was ready. Many more would be needed.

Down came another tree. The woods were filled with the crashing sound. Tree after tree fell. The short winter day was soon over. Evening was coming on.

The woods grew dim and dark. The men were weary and hungry. It was time to stop work.

Two men tied a rope to one of the beams and dragged it down to the shore. Thomas wanted to help. He only seemed to get in the way.

"Wherever I step I fall over that boy!" cried one man. "He is everywhere and always in the way!"

Thomas stood back with a sigh.

"Go get your firewood," said his father softly. "Carry as big a load as you can, and keep out of the men's way. Use your head, son."

Some of the men spent the night in small bark huts that they had built. Thomas went back to the ship. It was warm in the little cabin of the *Mayflower*. His mother had hot food ready. When he had eaten, Thomas leaned over the tiny new baby. The boy's hands were red with the cold, but the baby gripped his finger.

"I never saw such little hands," said Thomas.

His father looked at the baby. His face was serious and grave.

"We must get a house built to keep the little ones warm and safe," he said. "There is no time to spare."

Chapter 2. LOGS INTO BEAMS

The ends of the beams were cut so that they would fit together. Holes were bored in them. Pegs were needed to hold the beams together.

The next day all the boys from the ship were set to work cutting pegs. A big fire blazed on the shore. The boys worked near it.

At first Thomas worked as fast as he could. But soon he grew tired. Smoke from the fire blew in his eyes. It seemed to him as though he had cut enough pegs to hold the world together!

Suddenly the sharp knife slipped and cut his hand. Thomas gave a cry as blood came from his finger.

61

"He is afraid of a little blood," laughed one boy.

Thomas frowned. He walked to the brook near by. He broke a hole in the ice. The cold water would stop the bleeding. Why did he cry out so easily? Why did he do everything wrong?

Just then Thomas forgot his troubles. His finger had stopped bleeding. He cut a strong willow branch that grew by the water. He bent it against his foot. What a fine bow it would make! He would make a bow to shoot as the Indians did!

Thomas bent the branch. Then he strung a piece of string across it. Now for an arrow! He chose a forked stick and sharpened the point.

"See what I have," he called, as he went back to the fire.

The boys crowded around him.

"Let's see you shoot," they said.

"Stand back!" Thomas answered.

He fitted the arrow to the bow. He pulled the string. The arrow sped through the air. It went faster and farther than Thomas had expected.

A man had just finished making a window for the new house. He had no glass, and so he had stretched heavy paper across the opening. The paper was oiled and would let in the light.

Thomas sent his arrow straight through the paper!

"See what you have done,
you rascal!" shouted the man.
"Have you no head to use? It's
a pity your father did not drop
you overboard!"

"I meant no harm, sir," said
Thomas. "I will do whatever I can to make up."

The man gave a grunt. The boy had pluck at any
rate.

"I'm splitting a log into planks to make the front
door," he said. "Hold this wedge for me."

Slowly Thomas put out his hand to hold the wedge.
He gripped the wedge tightly and he tried to hold it
still. The man raised his hammer. But it was hard for
the boy to hold his hand still with the hammer so close
to his fingers.

Up went the hammer ready for a blow. It was too
much for Thomas! Before he knew what he was
doing, he jumped back. He dropped the wedge.

"Here's a pretty mess!" cried the man. "You can shoot an arrow through a window and spoil a day's work. But you are afraid to hold a wedge! Get away with you. You are more trouble than you are help!"

Sadly, Thomas went back to cutting pegs. Would he ever learn to use his head?

Ellen joined him by the fire. She was just his age. He always watched out for Ellen. She had no father or mother. She had come to help one of the women on the *Mayflower*. She seemed little and alone. She held her long cape close around her, but she looked cold and white.

The boys began to laugh at Thomas. Suddenly Ellen's eyes grew big and dark. She turned on the boys and she stamped her foot.

"He is better than any of you!" she cried. "You wait and see! You laugh and you make fun, but there is not one of you as quick and as kind as Thomas."

Ellen turned and ran back to the women. They were heating water in a big iron kettle over an open fire for their washing.

Chapter 3. THE HOUSE RAISING

At last the frame for the new house was ready to be raised.

Everyone gathered to help or to watch. At least everyone came who was well enough to be up. Many of the people lay ill and weak because of the long trip and poor food and the cold winter weather.

Thomas stood by Ellen. He was eager and excited as he watched the men working. How much he wanted to help!

But his father said softly, "Keep out of the way, son. You are too young for this heavy work."

One side of the frame was ready to be lifted into place. The men had long forked poles. They used them to lift the side into place. They struggled and strained as they raised the heavy load.

A man climbed carefully up the frame. Then the next side was raised. The man tried to reach it so that he could fasten the two sides together.

But the second side would not go where it should.

"Push it a little nearer!" shouted the men below. "No, easy there! That's too far!"

It seemed as though the frame were teasing them. It seemed as though it did not want to go into place.

If only the man had an extra hand. He must hold on with one hand while he reached for the second side with the other. He leaned over as far as he dared.

"Hold it! Hold it!" cried the men below.

The heavy frame began to tip! If it fell, there would be much hard work lost. People gasped with horror. The men struggled to hold up the frame. They needed the house so badly. They had worked so hard!

Then Thomas sprang forward. He could see clearly just what should be done. He knew he could jerk that frame into place. Before he thought what he was doing, he cried out, "I can fix it!"

"You!" cried a man. "You will only make trouble!"

But Thomas had darted forward. He started up the frame like a cat. He was light and small. A second man could not go up the frame without tipping it. Perhaps a boy could.

People held their breath as they watched him. Some called to him to come back. Some shouted to him to go on. As he reached the top of the frame, Thomas felt dizzy. He did not like high places. He stopped for a minute. Then he saw Ellen below. She was waving her hand and calling to him, "Go on! Go on, Thomas!" On he went.

In another minute he had pulled the frame into place. The holes fitted neatly, one right over the other.

66

In went the pegs to hold the two sides together. The frame stood strong and firm.

Thomas crept back. His hands were full of splinters. His clothes were torn. But he was happy. He was happier than he had ever been.

"The boy was as quick as a cat!" people said. "He has saved the house! He used his head this time! He is one to watch!"

Thomas slipped to Ellen's side. She smiled at him proudly. He stood beside her as they watched the last beams raised and hammered into place.

"You have torn your jacket," whispered Ellen. "But I'll mend it for you."

When the frame of the house was up, planks were fastened to the beams to make the sides. Logs split in half made the floor. The roof was thatched with bundles of coarse reeds tied with grapevines.

A big fireplace was built of stone. The chimney was of small logs covered with clay to keep them from burning. A strong pole of green wood was put across the chimney to hold the kettles.

It was an exciting day when the first fire was lighted in the new house. Women hurried here and there unpacking chests and cooking food. The boys ran back and forth carrying loads from the shore into the house. Then big iron kettles were hung over the fire. Soon the good smell of food filled the room. The house was done!

There were only one house and a few bark huts, but the people could live together this first winter. They had been together in the cabin of the *Mayflower*. They were used to living together.

Later each family would have its own house.

And so the town of Plymouth was started.

The first year was very hard for the Pilgrims, just as it had been hard for the people in Jamestown. Many died. But the well people cared tenderly for those who were ill. They worked hard. They prayed to God for His help.

Then one day an Indian walked into town. Children ran in fear and hid behind their mothers. Men reached for their guns. But the Indian raised his hand as a sign of peace. He came as a friend.

Later he came again with another Indian, who had been to England and spoke some English. The Indians helped the Pilgrims to plant corn. They showed them how to put a small fish in each corn hill so that the plant would grow well. They gave them seeds of beans and pumpkins.

In the fall, when the corn and beans and pumpkins were ripe, there was happiness in Plymouth. There would be food, not much, but some, for the winter. A day was set for thanksgiving.

A great Indian chief and ninety Indians came to the little town for that thanksgiving feast. They brought wild turkeys and five deer.

It was our first Thanksgiving Day. It was a day of feasting. It was a day of prayer as well.

HOW THE PILGRIMS BUILT THEIR HOUSES

1.

First, men chose tall oak trees. Thirty or forty trees were needed for one house. The men chopped the trees down.

2.

Boys helped chop off branches. Then the men cut the sides of the logs square for beams. They used their sharp axes.

3.

Ends of beams were cut so that they would fit neatly together. Pegs were used instead of nails. Pegs were driven through holes to hold the beams in place.

4.

Some of the logs were split into planks. The men pounded wedges into the logs. The wedges split the logs into planks. Saws were used to cut the planks.

5.

6.

When one side of the house had been put together, the men came to raise it. They pushed up the frame with poles.

Doors and windows were made. If there was no glass, oiled paper was used. A wooden latch held the door shut.

7.

8.

The roof was thatched with bundles of straw or reeds. The bundles were laid in rows and tied in place. The rows overlapped.

The fireplace was made of stone. The first chimneys were made of logs covered with clay. It was a happy day when the first fire was lighted.

73

Things to Talk About

1. Have you ever seen a house being built? What was being used to make it? What is your house made of?

2. Arrange an exhibit of things that are used to make houses. Bring small pieces of wood, some nails, brick, stone, cement, wire, glass.

3. What things did the Pilgrims have to use in making their houses?

4. Today we use machines to help make houses. Some of the machines are:

bulldozers	steam shovels
derricks	cement mixers

   Tell what each machine does. Which one do you think would have been most useful to the Pilgrims?

5. Tell what the Pilgrim boys and girls did to help. What can you do at home to help?

6. How do you think the Pilgrim children felt when the first Indian walked into Plymouth?

7. How did the Indians help the Pilgrims?

Things to Do

1. Make Indian headbands. Cut a strip of strong paper two inches wide. Cut out two feathers. Color them. Paste them on the band. Fasten the band with a clip.

2. On the blackboard draw a map of your schoolhouse and the streets near it. Draw in some of the houses. If you live nearby, show how you come to school.

3. On a large map find where you live. Then find St. Augustine, Jamestown, and Plymouth. Which place is nearest to your home? Have you ever been to one of these places, or do you know someone who has?

4. Find the number of the page on which each one of these pictures is.

    a. A Pilgrim house
    b. Boys cutting pegs
    c. Thomas shooting an arrow
    d. Thomas climbing the frame

5. Make up a play about the First Thanksgiving.

Things to Find Out

1. Read page 71 again. Copy on a piece of paper the words listed below that tell what the Pilgrims had to eat on Thanksgiving.

deer meat	corn	ice cream
strawberries	turkey	oranges
pumpkins	beans	salad

2. Find two words on page 68 that are made up of two shorter words. What two words make *Thanksgiving?*

3. On page 68 when someone said, "The boy was as quick as a cat," what did he mean?

He scratched like a cat.	He climbed quickly like a cat.
He mewed like a cat.	He forgot to be afraid.

4

Pioneers from Holland

A STORY OF DUTCH PIONEERS

Pioneers
from Holland

Pioneers from Holland came to this new land. People who live in Holland are called Dutch. The Dutch pioneers started their town where New York City stands today. They named it New Amsterdam after the Dutch city of Amsterdam.

As soon as they could, the people in New Amsterdam built Dutch houses like the houses in Holland. Soon they built a big Dutch windmill. Blue-eyed Dutch children played near the water.

Dutch mothers scrubbed the floors of their houses and tried to keep them as clean as the houses in old Amsterdam.

The Dutch pioneers had an easier time than the people in Jamestown and Plymouth. Dutch traders had been coming for some years to trade for furs with the Indians. They had built a few rough houses and started a fort. When the first fathers and mothers and children arrived, they found a fort and a few rough houses ready for them.

Then, one day, a ship sailed into the harbor with a very special load. The sea gulls flew about it, crying with surprise. Indians paddled out in their canoes to look in wonder.

The ship was loaded with cows and sheep and pigs. They were pioneers too!

It was a great day for New Amsterdam when that ship sailed into the harbor. There were several islands in the harbor. One large island was very close to the mainland. The ship stopped near it. There were no pastures ready for the animals on the mainland. The precious animals would be safer on the island at first.

What was it like on that day? How did the Dutch people feel? What did the Indians think? How had the Dutch sailors managed to bring cows so far?

The next story will tell you.

Peter and His Cow Trinka

Chapter 1. THE LANDING

Peter stood beside his cow Trinka. There was a smile on his face. There would have been a smile on Trinka's face if cows could smile. The trip from Holland to America was safely over.

"But really Trinka hardly knew she was not standing in her own barn," said Peter proudly. "She is a wonderful cow. She gives more cream than milk. She is gentle and kind. Her calves are just like her."

Peter's sister Juliana stood beside him. She was four years old. She agreed with all he said.

There were a few sheep and goats and pigs aboard, but the hold of the ship was filled with cows. No other cow could compare with Trinka!

Trinka had switched her tail and mooed gently all the way across the Atlantic Ocean. She had been well cared for. Big tanks to hold water had been built into the ship. Each day Peter had pumped up water for Trinka to drink and carried it to her in a pail. Clean white sand covered the water tanks.

Each cow had her own stall. Each cow stood in her own stall on the pure white sand. There was plenty of sweet hay aboard for the cows to eat. An extra ship sailed nearby with extra water and extra hay.

Each cow had a man or boy to care for her. Two of the precious animals had died at sea. It was a sad thing! But the rest were well and fat.

Trinka had never looked more beautiful.

"One would think she were going to the Fair," sighed Peter.

Peter had brushed her coat until it shone. He had rubbed her horns and hoofs. Juliana had given him her best red ribbon. He had tied it on Trinka's tail.

Now Trinka was ready to land in this strange new country. Peter led her out on deck.

He could see the thatched roofs of the tiny town of New Amsterdam near the water's edge. Woods came close about it. Were there Indians in those woods? What would the Indians say to Trinka, and what would Trinka say to the Indians?

But the cows were not to land in New Amsterdam. There were no pastures ready near that town. The cows might wander into the woods and be killed by wolves or bears. Peter trembled at the thought. He would fight any bear or wolf that came near Trinka!

The cows were to be landed on a small island in the harbor. The island was a safer place for them than New Amsterdam until pastures were ready. The ship sailed close to the shore of the small island. Planks were laid from deck to land. There were loud mooings and shouting and much noise. Some of the animals did not wish to go ashore.

Juliana ran to her mother and stayed close to her. Peter watched anxiously while his father and the other men pushed and pulled the animals down the plank. At last it was Trinka's turn.

"Trinka, little one," whispered Peter. "Come with me, Trinka. Do not be afraid!"

He led her gently toward the plank.

"Come, little one," urged Peter.

But Trinka would not come. She mooed and she turned back. She had decided that she did not want to be a pioneer. She wanted to go back to Holland.

"Get off there!" shouted a man.

Never had Trinka been spoken to in so rough a way. She tossed her head wildly.

82

"Please, Trinka, take just one little step for me!" Peter begged.

Suddenly something happened that surprised both Peter and Trinka. A pig ran loose. Men tried to catch it, but it is easier to catch lightning than a pig. It ran squealing toward the plank.

Right between Trinka's legs ran the pig. Trinka gave a bellow of surprise. She ran down the plank as fast as she could go. Peter was in the way. There was no place for him to go except into the water. There was a great splash. Trinka and the pig reached land. Peter did not.

"Help! Help!" shouted the people. "Save the boy!"

They pulled Peter from the water.

"To think that Trinka would do this to me!" thought Peter as he stood with water running off him. "Before all the world you give me a ducking! Oh, Trinka! Think of the hay and water I have carried for you!"

His mother hurried Peter to the cabin for dry clothes. Juliana looked seriously at him with her big blue eyes. When he was dressed again, she followed him out on deck. Together they stood watching the animals galloping around the island. They could tell Trinka by the red ribbon on her tail.

At last the animals grew tired and settled down. Trinka lay down beneath a tree. She was glad to find that she had a little cud left. It was a wonder!

Slowly she began to chew.

Chapter 2. NEW AMSTERDAM

A few days later, a ship loaded with horses arrived. Peter watched the men unload them. His father and mother and Juliana had gone ashore to stay with friends in New Amsterdam. Peter was still living on the ship. He wished to be near Trinka. Each day he went ashore to be with her.

The small island seemed alive with animals. Indians paddled out to look at the wonder. They had never dreamed there were such beasts. For the Indians had no horses or cows until the white men brought them across the ocean.

There were deer and buffaloes and wolves and bears in this new land. But those animals are not good ones to tame. You cannot drive a buffalo. You cannot milk a bear.

There was not enough grass on the small island for so many animals.

"We must take the horses and cows across to New Amsterdam where there is more grass for them to eat," said the men. "It will be dangerous in the woods with no pastures or fences ready. The boys will have to stay with them and watch them carefully."

"How will the animals get over?" asked Peter.

"We will carry some of the animals over in small boats," said the men. "Some of the animals can swim."

"Trinka could never swim," cried Peter in horror. "I do not believe that Trinka knows how to swim!"

"Get her into a boat, then," called the men.

They were pulling one cow in backward by her tail.

Peter talked gently to Trinka. He explained everything to her while she slowly chewed her cud.

She had lost her red ribbon. Peter thought that an Indian boy had taken it. He saw two Indian boys in a canoe near the island. One had a red ribbon round his head. The Dutch boy and the Indian boys looked at each other with interest.

86

The Indian boys looked at Peter's heavy wool suit and wooden shoes. Peter looked at the Indian boys. They wore only moccasins and strips of deerskin. As he looked, one Indian boy dived from the canoe into the water. He swam swiftly toward the mainland.

So now, as Peter led Trinka toward the boat, she had no ribbon on her tail. She had burrs in her coat, and her hoofs were muddy, but she was still a fine cow.

"Come into the boat with me, Trinka," said Peter softly.

But the little boat rocked up and down on the waves. Trinka did not like its looks.

"There, there, little one," murmured Peter.

Then an idea came to him. If Trinka could not see the boat, she would not be afraid.

He pulled off his coat. Under it he wore his best linen shirt. Peter took the shirt off carefully. He tied it about Trinka's head and over her eyes.

"Come, Trinka!" he said firmly.

But Trinka had other plans. She could see nothing. It had become dark. Clearly it was night. She would lie down and go to sleep.

The men in the boat began to laugh. It was too much for Peter. His patience was gone!

"Get up!" Peter said sharply to Trinka.

But Trinka only chewed her cud.

Peter grasped her tail and gave it a pull. Trinka started to get up, but then she settled back again. Peter did something that he had never expected to do. He gave Trinka a kick with his wooden shoe.

Trinka was so surprised that she scrambled to her four feet. Peter gave a tug at the rope. Down to the boat went Trinka. Peter gave a sigh of relief as she stood with her head on his shoulder. She slowly chewed her cud as the boat moved across the water.

Mother and Juliana were on shore waving to him as he landed. Peter quickly took his shirt off Trinka's head and put it on himself. It was wrinkled, but it was still as white as snow.

Proudly he led Trinka through the little town of New Amsterdam. Dutch children stopped playing to run along beside him and cheer. Dutch mothers stopped scrubbing their floors to run to their doors.

"As fine a cow as any in Holland!" they cried. "A wonderful cow! Now we shall have milk and thick yellow cream and butter and fat cheeses."

"This is a fine thing for the town," said the men as they smoked their long Dutch pipes.

"The rest of the cows will be over before night," called Peter happily. "And horses and sheep and pigs as well!"

Chapter 3. "COME QUICKLY!"

Each morning Peter and two other boys drove the cows to graze outside the town. Each morning Peter went through the narrow streets of the little town. He blew on a cow's horn. People ran to open their barn doors. Out came the cows to follow Trinka.

All day Peter and the boys watched the cows carefully. It was pleasant at the edge of the woods. Often Indians came by with loads of beaver furs to sell in New Amsterdam. Often hunters came past.

At the end of the day, the boys drove the cows home. Each cow knew its own barn. Dutch women ran to their kitchen doors. The doors were cut in half. There were no screen doors in those days. The lower half of the door was shut to keep cows or pigs from coming into the kitchen by mistake. The top half of the door stood open for air and light.

Out ran the Dutch women as Peter came by with the cows. Each woman carried a milking pail to hold the milk from the cows.

One day the cows wandered farther into the woods than usual. Peter was troubled. The boys ran after the cows and drove them back. When it was time to start home, something dreadful happened. Some of the cows would not go. Some walked slowly as though in pain. Some mooed loudly.

Peter was worried. He ran on ahead for help.

"Come quickly!" he shouted to the first men he saw. "All is not well with the cows!"

The men dropped their work and came running.

"What has happened?" they shouted.

"What is the matter?" they called.

Peter could only point to the cows. Some were lying down. Some were groaning. Peter was thankful to see that Trinka was still on her feet.

"Drive the well cows home, Peter," called the men. "We will see what we can do for these poor beasts."

Peter hurried along the streets with the well cows. He drove those he had with him to their barns. People called to him from every side.

"Where are our cows?" some asked anxiously. "Why didn't you bring all the cows home?"

No one slept in New Amsterdam that night. Twenty of the cows were ill. Twenty of the precious cows that had come so far and been tended so carefully. It was a sad thing indeed!

"They must have eaten some strange weed," said the men. "It has poisoned them. There is little we can do."

In the barn Peter sat beside Trinka. He sat and watched every breath she took. Not for a moment would he leave her. Had Trinka eaten the poison?

"Oh, my Trinka! Oh, my little Trinka!" whispered Peter.

Juliana brought him his supper, but he could hardly eat. She brought him fresh fried cakes that his mother had just made for him. But Peter could not even touch them. He held a lantern in his hand and he looked

91

Trinka over from head to tail. She seemed calm and peaceful. She was chewing her cud. But perhaps the poison had not yet begun to work.

A neighbor brought sad news. Several of the cows had died. Peter gave a groan. He looked at Trinka.

"You had better go to your bed, Peter," said his father.

Peter shook his head. He would not leave Trinka.

"Please don't die, Trinka!" he whispered.

At last Trinka lay down to sleep. Peter settled on the hay beside her. Once she had a bad dream and gave a loud groan. Peter jumped to his feet in fear.

92

But she only turned over and went to sleep again.

In the morning Juliana found Peter sound asleep, with his head on Trinka's back. But Trinka was safe. She was as strong and well as ever.

It was a sad procession that went to pasture the next day. Nineteen cows were dead. But the others were alive and safe. Trinka led the way down the street. Peter and the boys drove the precious animals to a different part of the woods.

The cows that did not die soon had calves. Before long the barns of New Amsterdam were filled with fine cattle. The housewives skimmed thick yellow cream from the pans of milk. They churned cream into butter. They made cheeses as big as your head.

It was a fine thing for New Amsterdam to have the cows.

But how did New Amsterdam become New York?

One day, when Peter was much older, and Trinka was a grandmother, a strange thing happened.

English warships came sailing into the harbor.

The Dutch governor of New Amsterdam at that time was named Peter Stuyvesant. Peter Stuyvesant had only one leg, so he wore a wooden one. He marched about the town with his wooden leg, and he ordered the men to fight the English.

But the English had more guns and cannon than the Dutch did. The Dutch men would not fight.

Peter Stuyvesant was a brave soldier. He stamped about the fort with his wooden leg. He ordered his men to fire, but they would not fight.

"It is foolish to shed blood for nothing," they said. "If we fight, our town will be destroyed. Our wives and children will be killed. We do not have enough guns or soldiers. There is no hope of winning!"

At last Peter Stuyvesant had to give in. He could not fight alone. Down came the Dutch flag from the fort. Up went the English flag.

The English ships had been sent by the brother of the king of England. He was called the Duke of York. So the name of New Amsterdam was changed to New York. And that is its name today!

But today the flag of New York City is still orange, white, and blue, like the old flag of Holland.

Each year New York grows larger and larger. Today it is the biggest city in the world.

HOW BUTTER WAS MADE

1.

First the cows were milked. Buckets of milk were carried to the house.

2.

The milk was poured into pans to set. Slowly the thick yellow cream rose to the top.

3.

A skimmer

The next morning the good housewife skimmed off the cream. Some of it she used on wild strawberries or puddings. The rest went into the churn.

4.

A dasher

When the churn was full of cream, it was time to begin the butter making. The dasher in the churn was worked up and down, up and down.

5.

It was hard work. At last little yellow lumps of butter began to show. Soon the butter was so thick that the dasher could hardly be moved.

6.

Then the butter was skimmed out. Buttermilk was left in the churn. It was good to drink. Everyone liked fresh butter on his bread, too.

7.

A paddle

The buttermilk was pressed out and the butter was well washed in fresh water. It was patted into shape with paddles.

8.

If the butter was to be kept for long, it was salted. Salted butter kept better. It was packed in little tubs.

Things to Talk About

1. Tell what you know about Holland.

2. If you have been on a farm, tell about the animals that you saw. Did you have a pet one?

3. Tell what New York City is like today. Do you know something about:

   The Statue of Liberty   The Empire State Building
   The subway   New York Harbor

4. Find New York City on the map. Why is so large a place only a little dot on the map?

5. Why were the animals not taken to New Amsterdam first? Why are fences important? Can you tell the class about electric fences?

6. Tell how New Amsterdam became New York. What is happening in the picture on page 94?

Things to Do

1. These are some of the important names in this book. See if you can read them aloud.

St. Augustine	New York	Plymouth
Peter Stuyvesant	Pilgrims	Florida
Captain John Smith	Jamestown	Holland
New Amsterdam	Pocahontas	Menéndez

2. Choose two committees to arrange exhibits.

   a. Make an exhibit of things about Holland. Draw pictures of windmills and Dutch people. Perhaps someone has a Dutch doll; or

98

b. Put up an exhibit of pictures of farms. Perhaps you can arrange a model of a farm and bring toy animals.

3. Which direction is north on your map? Which direction is north in your school room?

4. If you can, bring a compass to school. If someone can bring a magnet and a needle, you can make a compass. Rub the needle on the magnet. Float the needle on a tiny bit of paper in a cup of water. The needle will swing toward north.

5. How would a compass help a sailor? How would it help someone in the woods?

Things to Find Out

1. Find a word on page 89 that is made up of two short words. Find another one on page 93.

2. Some words end with *ful*. Tell what these words mean.

thankful   wonderful   dreadful   careful

To which of the words given below can you add *ful*, and in this way make a longer word?

help   slow   thought   good   peace   fear   joy

3. Make up riddles about the names on this page. Make them something like this. "Who was the man that was captured and almost killed by the Indians. He helped start Jamestown. He said, 'Anybody that does not work, shall not eat.'"

5

Pioneers from France

A STORY OF TRAVELING BY CANOE

Pioneers from France

Pioneers came to this country from France, as well as from Spain and England and Holland.

French pioneers sailed up the great river to the north of our country. They named it the St. Lawrence River.

Other French pioneers explored the middle of our land. They found the Great Lakes. They went down the Mississippi River.

The French soon learned to use the Indian birchbark canoes. The canoes were useful boats. They were a fine gift that the Indian gave to the white man. No other kind of boat was so light and yet so strong as the canoe.

Pioneers could take the canoes from the water and carry them from one river to another. They could paddle them in shallow water in small rivers. They could pull the canoes on shore and sleep under them at night.

So French hunters paddled canoes up the rivers. French traders bought canoe loads of furs from the Indians. French priests went by canoe among the Indians to teach them the white man's ways.

The French treated the Indians well. Most of the Indians liked the French people. They came often to the French towns to trade.

In 1701 a Frenchman started a little town called Detroit. He built a fort and a few houses. His name was Cadillac.

Today, Detroit is a big city. Thousands and thousands of cars are made there each year. Thousands of airplanes are made in the factories. Huge steamers bring iron and coal to make the cars and airplanes. Docks line the shore.

It was very different long, long ago when the first white men came to Detroit. Huge trees grew by the water's edge. Wild animals came down to drink. Birchbark canoes slipped quietly through the water.

What was it like, paddling to Detroit in a canoe? The next story, "The Pioneer Doll," will tell you.

The Pioneer Doll

Chapter 1. THE PORTAGE

Paddling canoes upstream was hard work!

All day the men pushed the canoes forward with their paddles. The canoes carried heavy loads. Marie sat with her mother in the middle of one canoe. Bundles of blankets and clothes, bags of food, axes and guns, were packed carefully around her. She leaned against a big iron kettle for a back.

In her arms Marie held the most precious thing she owned. It was her doll. It was a beautiful doll. It was dressed in silk and velvet like a queen. It had come from France. Marie called it Lady Claire.

104

Marie kept the doll well wrapped in a heavy cape. Every now and then she peeked at her. Lady Claire must not get too warm or her wax face and hands might melt. She must not get too cold or they might crack. No water must splash her lovely dress.

Marie held the doll carefully. Then she glanced ahead. The great forest trees bent their branches over the water. The canoe swung round a curve in the river.

There, under a giant oak tree, stood a deer drinking! Marie held her breath. The deer was so beautiful. One of the men reached for his gun. A shot rang out. The deer leaped into the air. It ran crashing through the bushes.

The man jumped ashore. Another shot sounded. Then all was still.

"It is such a pity!" sighed Marie's mother. "But we must eat!"

That night they made camp by the river side. Marie helped her mother cook tender bits of deer meat. They stuck the meat on green sticks and held them over the coals.

It was fun living outdoors when the weather was good. It was fun, except for the mosquitoes! There had been no mosquitoes in France.

"I wish they were all buzzing at the bottom of the sea!" cried Marie.

Her father threw damp leaves on the fire to make smoke to drive them away. But the smoke got in her eyes. Marie gave a sigh. Then she unwrapped the Lady Claire to see if she were dry and safe.

Day after day and week after week, the canoes went on and on. There was one day that Marie would never forget. The canoes had gone as far as they could on the first river. Now the men were going to carry them across to another river. This was the first portage.

The "portage" meant the "carrying." There was plenty of carrying to be done. All morning the men and boys went back and forth carrying loads.

106

At first Marie and her mother sat under a great tree by the river bank. Marie made a garden in a bed of green moss for the Lady Claire. She put ferns and violet plants around her. She made a seat of white stones. There sat the Lady Claire, smiling and lovely.

"I will carry over all the cups and the bowls," said her mother. "And see that all the little things are safe."

Then she called to Marie to help her. Marie followed her down the trail. Her arms were full.

Everything was now across the portage. The men slipped the light canoes into the water. They piled the loads in. The hard work was over.

Suddenly Marie remembered the Lady Claire. She had left her on her mossy throne. Marie turned and ran back down the forest trail as fast as she could go. No one saw her. Her feet made no sound on the thick leaves. She ran as fast as she could.

Then Marie gave a sigh of relief. There sat her doll. A red leaf had fallen into her lap. Her flowers were fresh and gay. She had never looked more lovely.

107

Suddenly there was a humming sound. A strange tiny bird darted out. Marie had never seen so small a bird. It looked like a jewel with tiny wings. It flew around the Lady Claire. Then it ran its long needle of a bill into the flowers.

Marie stood watching the tiny thing. She had never seen anything like it before.

Suddenly she remembered that she was alone. The forest seemed very big and lonely. She snatched up the Lady Claire. The humming bird darted away. Marie started running back through the woods. She ran wildly along the trail.

Perhaps the others had gone on and left her! Perhaps no one had missed her! Then Marie saw someone coming toward her down the trail. It was her brother Pierre. She started to shout to him. Then she stopped. She would not let him see how frightened she had been. She had been running about like the silly sheep at home. That was how people got lost in the woods.

"I went back to get my doll," she said.

"Why are you carrying her upside down?" asked Pierre.

It was then that Marie saw that she held the lovely Lady Claire with her head down. Her little white kid boots waved in the air.

Quickly she turned the doll right side up!

Chapter 2. THE PEACE PIPE

When the portage was over, the canoes started downstream. Going downstream was far easier for the men than paddling upstream. The river carried the canoes swiftly along.

But the men who steered the canoes must watch out. The water ran swiftly. There were rocks in the river. The light canoes might strike against one. They might be tipped over, or have a great hole torn in the bottom.

Marie sat in the canoe with the Lady Claire in her lap. The doll was smiling and beautiful. Pierre sat in the same canoe near her. Marie told Pierre about the humming bird. There were many new sights and sounds in this strange land. The first time that Pierre had caught a firefly for her, Marie had thought it would burn her hand.

During the afternoon, rain started to fall. Marie wrapped the Lady Claire in a blanket. Then she pulled a blanket over her own head.

"We had best make camp now," said the men.

But as they turned the canoes toward shore, one of them hit against a sharp point of rock. There was a loud ripping sound. Marie peeked out from her blanket. She could hear shouts. She could see men in the water hanging onto a canoe. Her father paddled swiftly to shore. Then he and Pierre hurried to try to help the other men. But it was too late.

There was a big hole in the canoe. The boat was fast filling with water. Some men managed to save part of the load that the canoe carried. They swam to shore with it. Other men tried to hold up the sinking canoe and pull it to shore.

"What will we do if we lose it?" cried Marie. "The other boats are full already."

"We will have to see," said her mother.

They watched anxiously. The swift, running water was carrying the canoe out of the men's reach. Soon it was lost. The men swam ashore wet and tired.

"We must get a fire burning to dry them," said Marie's mother.

Everything was soaked. The blanket rolls were wet. The salt bag was wet. There was no need to mix water with the corn meal to make corn bread! The corn meal was wet already.

The men were tired, but they started cutting pine branches to make huts for the night. Marie and her mother worked to get the fire going. It was hard to find dry leaves and twigs.

Pierre took a hatchet to chop open an old log for dry wood. Suddenly he saw something moving in the misty forest. For a moment he stood perfectly still. Then he walked to his father and said in a soft voice, "There are Indians near, I think."

Marie and her mother heard, but they made no sound.

"Keep on with what you are doing," whispered her mother to Marie.

Marie fed chips of wood to the fire. It was hard to hold her hand still. She could not help looking into the misty greenness of the wet forest. Who was there? Who was watching her?

Word that Indians were near went from one man to the next.

"No one is to shoot unless I give the word," said her father softly. He had been among the Indians before. He knew their ways.

Then Marie saw him take something from a leather bag. It was a long pipe. Feathers and beads hung from it, and a wolf's tail. It was a peace pipe. Once, long ago, an Indian chief had given it to her father.

Now Marie saw her father hold the pipe above his head. She heard him call out strange words. He was calling to the Indians to come and sit by his campfire. He was inviting them to feast with him.

Pierre threw more wood on the fire. At last the bright flames blazed up. The fire seemed to warm a little space in the wet, dripping woods.

A tall figure slipped to the fireside. Quietly the tall Indian seated himself. Then came another and another. Marie held her mother's hand, but she stood silently.

The Indians were painted in gay colors. They wore a few feathers in their hair. Strings of bear teeth hung at their necks. As each man came to the fire, Marie's father welcomed him.

"We are your friends," the white man said. "Our fire is your fire."

Fish and deer meat were cooked. The peace pipe was lighted. It was passed from one man to the next.

Then Marie's father told of the lost canoe. He offered blankets and knives and beads for another canoe. He made a pile on the ground and pointed to it.

The chief nodded his head. He had a canoe, a good canoe, that he would sell.

112

Marie's father asked the Indians to go with them to Detroit. There were many Frenchmen in Detroit. They had blankets and knives and kettles and bright little mirrors. They would trade them for furs.

The Indians talked among themselves. They had furs to sell. Yes, they would go with their new white friends. In the morning, they would bring their women and children. They would go to see what the white men had.

As the men talked, Marie sat with her mother in the little hut of pine branches that the men had built. It was open toward the fire.

Marie was growing too sleepy to stay awake any longer. The light from the fire danced against the wet black forest. It lighted the faces of the Indians. It all seemed like a dream to Marie.

She looked to see that the Lady Claire was warm and dry in her cape. Then Marie's eyes closed and she fell asleep.

Chapter 3. DETROIT

In the morning the woods seemed filled with Indians. Canoes were waiting at the shore. There were Indian women and Indian children with black hair and big dark eyes. They stared at Marie.

The rain had stopped. The sun was shining. Marie stood near the canoe ready to start. She unwrapped the Lady Claire to let her see the world.

An Indian woman saw the doll. She cried out with pleasure. The women and children crowded about the boat. They wanted to pat the soft velvet dress. They wished to look at the tiny boots. They wanted to stroke the doll's hair.

114

"Let them see Lady Claire," said Marie's mother softly. "I do not think they will hurt her."

Marie held her breath while the Indians passed the doll from one to another. But they were gentle with her. The Lady Claire looked surprised, but she was not hurt. It was strange to see the little French doll with all her fine clothes in the hands of Indian children.

But there was no more time to admire the doll. The canoes were ready to start. There was hurry and excitement. One canoe after another slipped quietly out onto the water. There were twenty of them. Five were filled with French people. The rest carried Indians.

The river grew wider as the canoes moved down it. Then, at last, they came out on a great lake.

"It looks like another ocean!" cried Marie.

Indeed, it seemed almost as large as an ocean. The canoes kept close to shore.

Sometimes the canoes raced each other. Sometimes the French sang as their paddles rose and fell. It was a gay sight to see so many graceful boats slipping through the water.

Then, one day, the canoes came to the river that led from one Great Lake to the next. There the little town of Detroit had been started.

"We will be in Detroit before the day is over!" said Pierre.

Suddenly the sky filled with great thunder clouds.

"Oh dear, must it rain again!" sighed Marie.

Thunder roared. Lightning flashed.

"Shall we go ashore?" asked the men.

"Let's keep on," said Marie's father. "We have not far to go."

The rain began to pour down upon them. The canoes kept close to shore so that they could land if they needed to. But no one wished to stop. Detroit was near! Friends were near! Dry houses and warm fires were near!

Suddenly a gun sounded. Marie thought it was more thunder, but it was not. The fort had been sighted. Another gun and another was fired from the canoes. The Indians looked frightened, but the white men pointed joyfully ahead to the fort.

There stood a big fort. There were log houses near. People were running down to the shore. A cannon roared in welcome.

Just as the canoe landed, the rain stopped. The sun came out.

"Look!" cried Marie.

The sun had made a rainbow. It curved in lovely colors across the sky.

116

WS

"It is a good sign!" cried everyone.

That night it seemed strange to Marie to sleep in a house again. It seemed queer to have a wooden floor under her feet. It seemed odd to be in a dry place when it rained. But soon she was settled and happy in her new home.

The Lady Claire sat safely on a high shelf. She smiled at everyone who came into the cabin. She smiled at the Indians and white people alike.

The Indians stayed for a week at the Frenchmen's fort. They traded their furs. They feasted and they danced around the campfire at night.

At last they were ready to go back to their forest homes. But they promised to come again. They promised to help the Frenchmen and to be their friends.

Just before they left, an Indian woman came to Marie. She smiled at Marie and she held out her hand. What did she have? Marie looked with surprise. What was it? The woman pointed to the Lady Claire.

Then Marie saw what the Indian woman had brought. It was a tiny pair of moccasins. They were made of deerskin as soft as silk. They had tiny beads on their toes. They were lined with the fur of a field mouse. They were moccasins for the Lady Claire.

And so the French pioneers paddled their birchbark canoes on the rivers and lakes in the middle part of our country. Often the French passed by the spot where the city of Chicago stands today. They explored the Great Lakes. They went down the Mississippi River.

Pioneers from France came to live in the central part of our country. Pioneers from Spain came to live in the southern part of our country. Pioneers from England came to live in the eastern part of our country. Pioneers from Holland and from many other lands came to many parts of this land.

How did all these different people become Americans?

How did the United States of America start to be a great country? The next story will tell you.

HOW BIRCHBARK CANOES WERE MADE

A tall white birch tree was found. It was chopped down with a stone ax, or a steel ax bought from the white man.

The bark was slowly peeled off with wooden wedges. The work must be done carefully. The bark must not be split.

A strong frame was made. The wood was soaked in hot water so that it could be bent. Each piece must curve just so.

Sticks were driven into the ground to hold the bark in the right shape while the men worked on it.

5.

The bark was sewed onto the frame with roots. Roots were tough and strong.

6.

Cracks were filled with pitch from pine trees. A canoe must not leak!

7.

The canoe was decorated with porcupine quills or paint. When a canoe was done it was a fine sight to see. It was strong but light.

8.

Strong, straight paddles were cut to paddle the canoe. The canoe could move swiftly and quietly through the water. It could carry heavy loads.

Things to Talk About

1. Find the St. Lawrence River on the map. Find the Great Lakes and the Mississippi River. What kind of mark is used on a map to show a river? Can you find other rivers on the map?

2. We have read about people from several different countries who came to this country. From what countries did they come? Find out what people were the first to settle near your home.

3. Have you ever camped out? Have you ever cooked outdoors? Tell what you did.

4. What does the word *portage* mean?

5. Why was it foolish for Marie to "run about like the silly sheep," when she was frightened in the woods? What should you do if you ever lost your way?

Things to Do

1. Choose some children to act out the scene that will show what happened when the Indians came to camp. Use your Indian headbands. Perhaps someone can bring an Indian costume. Make a peace pipe. End the scene with an Indian dance. Perhaps someone can bring a drum.

2. Dress a doll to look like the Lady Claire.

3. Find the short words in these long words and tell what they mean.

deerskin	birchbark	campfire	Frenchmen
downstream	upstream	fireside	rainbow

122

4. Why was the birchbark canoe so useful to the pioneers? Draw a picture of one.

Things to Find Out

1. Read page 113. What did the Indians have that the pioneers wanted to buy?

2. What did the pioneers have that the Indians wanted?

3. Perhaps someone could bring bits of fur for an exhibit. Feel of the different kinds of fur. Which kind would you use for a baby's cover? Which kind would you use for a man's coat?

4. On page 116, find a word that means something that flashes through the sky.

5. On page 118, find a word that means a kind of shoe.

6. Study the pictures on pages 120 and 121 that show how a birchbark canoe is made. Play that you are an Indian father teaching his son how to make a canoe.

7. Draw a picture of something that is made in Detroit today.

8. Which of these sentences tell about the Lady Claire?

> She had little white kid boots.
> She was made of rubber.
> She was dressed in silk and velvet.
> Her face and hands were of wax.
> She was dressed like a baby doll.

6

How the United States Began

THE STORY OF A BOY WHO SAW
GEORGE WASHINGTON MADE PRESIDENT

How the United States Began

Over two hundred years had now passed since Spanish pioneers had landed in St. Augustine.

Over a hundred and fifty years had passed since Pocahontas saved Captain John Smith.

But still there was no United States of America. There was no flag with red and white stripes, and white stars on blue.

People in the English part of the country began to complain about the laws that England was making. For several years there was talk and trouble. Then a war began between England and some of the people in this country. We call this war the American Revolution.

A great man was put in charge of the American soldiers. His name was George Washington.

The Fourth of July is our country's birthday. On the Fourth of July in 1776, men met together in Philadelphia. They decided that our country should be a free country.

126

There was a big bell hanging in the hall in Philadelphia where the men met. News of what had been decided was told to the people of Philadelphia. The big bell rang out loud and clear. We call that bell the "Liberty Bell."

But there was a long and terrible war before our country was free. General Washington led his men through much misery and many hardships. At last the war ended. Washington and his men won. The English soldiers left this country. The United States was a free land.

It was a very small country at first. There were only thirteen states. Our first flag had thirteen stars on it, one for each state. Today we have forty-eight states, and forty-eight stars on our flag.

When the war ended, our country had no President. At last it was decided that one must be chosen. There was no question who that man should be. The first President of the United States was to be George Washington.

There was no city of Washington in those days. The city of Washington had not yet been built. So the new President was to live in New York City.

The next story will tell you of the day, April 30, 1789, when Washington was made President.

The First President

Chapter 1. NATHAN'S PONY

Nathan started off from his home on his pony. The air was cool and sweet with the smell of April flowers. The sun was just rising.

His mother stood at the farmhouse door to wave good-by.

"Watch out that your pony does not step into a hole," she called. "The road is rocky."

Nathan kissed her good-by. She looked at the tall, strong boy with pride. Then she said, "I wish your father were alive to see this day!"

Nathan, too, was thinking of his father. He wished with all his heart that his father were riding beside him into New York City to see General George Washington made President.

Nathan's father had been an officer in Washington's army. He had been killed in the American Revolution.

128

Nathan had been only a small boy, but he could still remember his father.

Thud, thud, thud, beat his pony's feet on the dirt road. The geese, chickens, and ducks of the farm were left behind. His dog followed him a little way. He begged to go along, but Nathan sent him back.

The road led through the woods. A rabbit hopped across the road. Birds sang in the trees. It was a lovely time of year.

The pony tried to turn in at a farmhouse, but Nathan kept it on the road. He had no time for calls this day. The pony gave a sigh, and trotted on.

Nathan thought of the stories that he had heard of Washington and the Revolution. Often soldiers met to talk. Sometimes they met at the mill where Nathan took wheat to be ground into flour. Sometimes they met at the inn to talk of the old days in the army.

The soldiers talked of the hard black days when it had seemed as though the war would never end. Sometimes there had been nothing to eat. Sometimes men had walked with bleeding feet through the snow because they had no shoes. Through all the hardships, Washington had led them.

Now the war was over. The United States of America was a free country. George Washington was to be made the first President. And Nathan was trotting along on his pony to see the great sight.

New York was a pleasant little city to visit on that bright April day. It was small compared with New York today. It was large compared with New Amsterdam. Many of the houses were of brick. They were two or three stories high. Trees lined the streets. There were gardens behind the houses.

Few of the streets were paved. There were holes in them, and mud when it rained. Pigs wandered here and there. Sometimes a cow ran loose. But this April day was a very special day. Everything in New York was in the best of order.

Flags and strips of bright cloth hung from the windows and balconies. Fine coaches drove through the streets. People wore their brightest and gayest clothes. Ladies had on wide full skirts and big bonnets. Men wore tight-fitting suits with ruffles of lace. Never had the city looked so bright and gay.

Nathan's pony was not sure he liked it all. The waving flags troubled him. He began to dance on his hind legs. But Nathan was a good horseman. He rode well. He spoke quietly to the pony and stroked its neck.

Just then a girl leaned out from a balcony. She held a big silk flag. Suddenly a puff of wind blew it out.

130

The pony gave a jump and reared. Then Nathan heard the girl cry out.

The wind had blown the flag from her hands.

"Oh, my flag!" she cried. "Someone catch it!"

Down fluttered the big flag. Nathan and his pony were just below the balcony. The flag covered them in a mass of stars and stripes.

The pony gave a jump that nearly sent Nathan over its head. Then it ran down the street at full gallop. Nathan could hear people screaming and dogs barking. He snatched up the flag with one hand. He waved it as he rode.

People began to clap and to cheer. He could not stop his pony. Around the town he rode waving the flag proudly above his head. At last the pony was too tired to gallop farther.

The pony's sides were covered with foam. It was panting and trembling. Nathan talked gently to it. Then he rode back to the house where the girl lived.

The same girl was leaning from the balcony. He saw that she was about his age. She had blue eyes and curly dark hair. Nathan handed her the flag.

"Thank you!" she cried. "You were wonderful! At first I thought the pony would throw you, but when I saw how well you rode, I was not afraid. Thank you for saving my flag."

"Come in and watch the great sights from our windows," said the girl's mother. "We will have a fine view of the balcony where General Washington will stand."

Nathan took his pony to the stable behind the house. He rubbed down its hot sides. He left it to rest.

"Come and help me hang out my flag," called the girl, whose name was Abigail. "I sewed every stitch of it myself."

It was a beautiful flag with its thirteen white stars on the blue ground, and its red and white stripes. Nathan helped fasten it firmly to the balcony so that it could not blow away again.

Chapter 2. THE PRESIDENT

A great shout went up from the street. Nathan and Abigail leaned over the railing of the balcony as far as they dared. People were cheering. Boys were throwing their hats in the air. The coach with General Washington had arrived.

"Which man is Washington?" cried Nathan.

"The tall one, the tall one with the white hair," said Abigail.

But it was too late. The men had climbed the steps and gone into the hall. Nathan gave a sigh of disappointment.

"You will see him later," said Abigail's mother. "He will come out on that balcony. He will stand there when he is made President."

There was a long wait, but Nathan and Abigail had plenty to do. The rooms were filled with people. A cold lunch was laid out with dishes of meats and cakes and puddings and coffee.

Nathan looked out of the window at the crowds below and above. Windows and roofs were crowded with people. He looked down toward the water at the end of the street. He could see the masts of sailing

ships. They were larger ships than the one that had
brought Peter and Trinka to New Amsterdam, but
they were still sailing ships. There were no steamships yet.

At last came sounds of warning. Nathan glanced
quickly at the building across the street. Men were
coming out on the balcony. Everyone pushed forward
to see.

"Careful! Don't fall out!" warned Abigail's mother.

But Nathan was not going to miss seeing George Washington this time!

Out onto the balcony came a group of men. Nathan's heart gave a great jump. There stood Washington! He was taller than the other men. He wore a plain brown suit. On his head was a white wig tied at the back.

Nathan gazed at the great man. This was the man with whom his father had fought. This was the man who had led his country to liberty.

Washington laid his hand upon the Bible. He was promising to serve his country wisely and well. He was promising to help the United States of America to be a land where people could live in peace and happiness.

Suddenly a flag was raised over the building. It was the signal. George Washington had become President! Cannons boomed. People cheered and shouted. Again and again the cannon roared. George Washington was President of the United States.

Suddenly Nathan found that a lump was rising in his throat. He could not cheer. He could not shout. Something gripped his heart. Tears were running down his face.

"Do not be ashamed," said Abigail's mother. "This is a great day. It is a solemn day. May we all be worthy of it!"

She wiped her own eyes.

Abigail was calling Nathan to come out onto the street with her. The two ran down the wide stairway. They watched President Washington walk along the street. He was going to St. Paul's chapel on Broadway. He was going to pray for help in the great work before him.

Nathan and Abigail watched the President as he walked through the streets of the little city. He was tall. He was more than six feet. He looked quiet and serious and patient.

He had already done a great work for his country. But there was still much to do.

Chapter 3. THE RIDE HOME

It was evening when Nathan started home on his pony. Abigail leaned from the balcony and waved to him.

"Come again," she called.

"I'll bring a basket of eggs and fresh butter from the farm," he promised. "And a basket of strawberries."

The road was crowded with people. Now and again fireworks flashed across the sky. Firecrackers and cannon still sounded. Nathan's pony danced along in excitement.

As the boy left the town, he turned to look back. He could see the large red brick house that had been made ready for President Washington. Abigail had told Nathan about it. It was filled with handsome furniture and fine china and shining silver.

There would be many fine dinners and balls given in that house while President Washington lived there. At night the ballroom would be lighted by hundreds of candles.

Nathan jogged along on his pony. He had seen the man whom his father loved. He had seen a sight

139

that he would never forget. Some day he would tell his children and grandchildren about it. Now he wanted to get home and tell his mother about it.

It was growing dark as Nathan rode through the woods. He and the pony were tired. They were hungry. Then the pony sniffed the air. He knew he was near home. He began to trot. His hoofs hit a stone, and a spark flew out.

At last, a light shone in the window of the little house. Nathan could see someone coming to the lighted door. He called to his mother as he led the pony to the stable.

It was good to sit on the big wooden settle by the fire. The bread that had been baked that day in the Dutch oven by the fireplace was warm and fresh. Nathan's mother put milk and cheese and fresh butter on the table.

While Nathan ate, he told his mother of the day. He had much to tell. He could not tell her everything that he had felt. But he told her as much as he could.

It was late when his story was done. The big logs in the fireplace had fallen into ashes. Nathan took out a red coal with a pair of iron tongs. He held it to the wick of a candle and blew on the coal. When the candle was lighted, he handed it to his mother. Then he lighted a candle for himself.

His mother covered the burning coals in the fireplace with ashes. The two went up the narrow, steep stairs of the little house.

Nathan's mother slept in a high bed with four posts. Dainty white curtains hung about it. Under that bed had been a wonderful place to hide when Nathan was a little boy. Once he had fallen asleep there. His mother had hunted the farm over, looking for him!

That had been long ago. Nathan was nearly as tall as his mother now. He kissed her good night and went into his own room.

Soon he was asleep. But in his dreams he still saw a tall, serious man with his hand on the Bible. He still heard the cry: "Long live George Washington, President of the United States!"

1.

2.

The fireplace was the most important part of the house. The fire gave heat and light, and cooked the food. A crane held the kettle over the fire.

Pothooks held the kettles to the crane. Long pothooks held the kettle in the hot flame. Short pothooks held the kettle farther from the fire.

3.

4.

Some iron pots stood on three little legs. They were set in the ashes. When cornbread was baked in one of these, a cover was put on and hot ashes piled on top.

Meat and turkeys were roasted in an open oven set in front of the fire. A handle turned the rod that held the meat, so that the meat would cook on both sides.

5.

6.

Frying pans often had long handles so that people would not have to get too close to the fire. The pans were used for cooking bacon and pancakes.

By the fireplace was an oven lined with brick. A hot fire was built in it. When the bricks were hot, the ashes were brushed out. The bread was put in with a long-handled shovel.

7.

8.

A warming pan hung by the fireplace. On winter nights, hot coals were put in it. It was used to warm cold beds.

A tin box inside the foot stove held hot coals. In church, on a trip, or in a cold room, foot stoves were a comfort.

Things to Talk About

1. Why do you think our country is called the United States of America?
2. Which state do you live in?
3. What did our first flag look like? How was it different from the flag we have today?
4. Tell some of the things that Nathan saw in New York that Peter would not have seen in New Amsterdam.
5. When the first President was chosen, the story says, "There was no question who that man should be." What does this sentence mean?
6. Where does our President live today?
7. What day is our country's birthday?

Things to Do

1. Choose some children to act out the scenes in this story. These scenes are not in the right order. Tell how they should come.
   a. Nathan tells his mother about the day in New York.
   b. Abigail leans from the balcony.
   c. Nathan's pony is frightened by the flag and runs away.
   d. People cheer and shout as Washington is made President.
   e. Nathan rides into New York City.
2. Find out all you can about George Washington. Perhaps you could invite someone from an older class to come and tell you about him.

144

3. Choose a committee to arrange a bulletin board exhibit. Find pictures of Washington. Find pictures of Mount Vernon, Washington's country home. Find pictures of the city of Washington today.

4. Put up a big piece of wrapping paper. Draw a big fireplace on it. Cut out as many of the things that were used for cooking as you can. Cut them out of heavy paper or tagboard and color them. Make a crane that will swing out from the fireplace so that you can lift off the kettles. Make pothooks. Make kettles of different sizes. Make a three-legged kettle to stand in the ashes. Make a warming pan and a foot stove.

Things to Find Out

1. Find the page on which each of these pictures is shown. Which one do you like best?

    The Liberty Bell
    Nathan and his pony covered by the flag
    Nathan and Abigail watch from the balcony
    People watch as George Washington is made President
    Washington enters St. Paul's Chapel
    Washington walks through the streets
    Nathan sits on a settle as he tells his mother about the day

2. Find out more about the Liberty Bell. Perhaps you can draw a picture of it. See the one on page 126. In what city is the Liberty Bell now?

7   Pioneers Going West

A STORY OF PIONEERS ON THE
WILDERNESS TRAIL

Pioneers
Going West

How did our country grow from a little country with thirteen states to a big country with forty-eight states?

The first thirteen states were along the Atlantic Ocean. Even before the American Revolution, people started going west. There was good land beyond the mountains in Kentucky.

It was hard to travel through the forests. Wild animals and Indians were in the woods. There were rivers to cross and no bridges. There were mountains to find a way through.

There was one pioneer named Daniel Boone. He had a gun named "Tick-licker." With his gun in his hand he explored in the new land of Kentucky.

Kentucky was a fine land. Part of it was covered with thick forest. Part of it was grassland. Buffaloes wandered across it. Deer and game were so thick that a hunter could hit without aiming, so men said!

148

Daniel Boone marked a trail to Kentucky. He called it the Wilderness Road. It was not really a road. It was so rough and wild that only people on foot or on horseback could follow it.

Part of the Wilderness Road followed an old Indian path. Part of it followed a buffalo trail. At the end of it was a log fort.

Before the American Revolution, only a few people came over the Wilderness Road. When the fighting was over, more and more people began to come.

What was it like, going west on this road?

Today you can drive a car where Indians once walked. You can fly in a plane above the weary miles where pioneers walked or rode on horseback.

In some ways, pioneers on the Wilderness Road had an easier time than the first people who came to Jamestown and Plymouth. The men knew how to hunt far better than those first pioneers. The women knew how to make better homes in the wilderness.

In other ways, pioneers going west on this road had a much harder time. No ships came sailing across the sea bringing news and friends from their old homes. When the woods closed about travelers on the Wilderness Road, they were very much alone.

What was it like, going west on Boone's Wilderness Road? The next story will tell you.

The Wilderness Trail

Chapter 1. THE JOURNEY DRESS

The Harris family were leaving their home in North Carolina. They were leaving the corn fields where Molly and John and big brother Jed had played hide-and-seek, and Baby Susan was always getting lost.

"This year we'll plant our corn in Kentucky," said Father.

People said that the land in Kentucky was fine and rich. People had talked so much that here was the whole Harris family getting ready to start. Six other families were going too. They were going over the Wilderness Road.

150

"Molly must have a new dress for the journey," her mother said. "It must be of good strong cloth. It will be torn and patched before we reach our new home. It had better be new to start with."

Molly gave a jump of joy. She had never had a really new dress before. Her dresses had been old ones of her mother's cut down. Now she was to have a new, new dress, a journey dress!

You did not get a dress in those days by just asking for one. No, indeed!

First Father sheared the sheep. The sheep did not like it. They baaed and they bleated. Father held them still as the shears went clip, clip, clip. When the clipping was over, the sheep looked very bare and

151

silly. But a big pile of dirty white wool lay on the ground.

The journey dress was begun!

Next Molly helped wash the wool. She carried pail after pail of water from the spring. She helped chop wood for a fire to boil the water. Then she scrubbed the wool in it until it was white and clean.

But the journey dress was only just begun!

Next they carded the wool. Every bit of straw or burr must be combed out. All the tangles must be straightened. At last the wool lay in a soft light pile. It was as soft as milkweed fluff.

But the journey dress was not done yet!

Next came the spinning. Round and round went the big spinning wheel. Carefully Molly fed in the wool, so that the yarn would be smooth and even. Back and forth she walked. Sometimes a girl walked twenty miles a day as she spun her yarn.

But the journey dress was not done yet!

In the evenings Molly wound up the yarn. Then it was ready to dye. A dye pot stood by the fire. There was blue dye in it.

"Don't make it too dark a blue," begged Molly.

Her mother dipped the wool. It came out a beautiful bright blue. Molly clapped her hands with pleasure.

But the journey dress was not done yet!

Mother worked at the heavy loom. She set it up with linen thread. Then she wove in the woolen yarn. Linen and wool made stronger cloth than wool alone. It was called linsey-woolsey.

Molly was not strong enough to weave. She cooked and washed and minded Susan and cleaned the house while her mother wove. Inch by inch the cloth grew.

"That's as nice a bit of cloth as ever I saw," said Father. "Are you making me a new shirt?"

There was a twinkle in Father's eye, but a sudden fear filled Molly's heart. Perhaps he needed a new shirt more than she needed a dress.

"I have clothes for you and the boys ready," said Mother. "And the shoemaker has made each one of you a new pair of shoes. This cloth is for Molly."

Molly gave a sigh of relief. She was going to have the new dress after all.

But the journey dress was not done yet!

Mother spread the beautiful blue cloth on the big table. She cut it with her precious shears. The dress must be long enough so Molly would have room to grow. Mother cut carefully. Then she sewed the dress by hand. The skirt was long and full. The waist was fitted. Molly had to stand while it was tried on. Father cut wooden buttons to fasten it.

At last the journey dress was done!

It was a very plain and simple dress, but it was a lovely color. It was just the color of Molly's blue eyes. Her light hair hung down her back in two pigtails. Molly held out the full skirt. She danced across the room. Baby Susan clapped her hands and laughed. Father took out his fiddle and played a tune for Molly to dance by.

Molly was ready for the journey.

Chapter 2. THE START

Johnny's new journey suit was made of deerskin.

He had shot the deer himself with his father's gun. He had soaked the deerskin in water and scraped off the hair. Then he had put it into a wooden tank of water and hickory bark. Six months it had soaked. This tanned the skin. It turned it into leather.

Mother had sewed his suit. She had made the shirt and trousers. She had left a fringe of deerskin hanging at the sides. She had made him a coon cap from the fur of a raccoon.

At his waist, Johnny wore a belt with a hunting knife and hatchet hanging from it. But Johnny did not have a gun. He wanted a gun more than anything else in the world.

"Wait till you are fourteen," said his father. "You are big for your age, but you are only twelve."

Every pioneer boy longed for the day when he would have a gun of his own. It meant that he had become a man and could take care of himself. But he must be a good shot before he could have a gun of his own.

There were other things besides guns to think of on this day! The hour for starting on the trip had arrived. Johnny held a pack horse while his father tied on a load.

Small Susan was to ride in a basket tied to one side of a horse. On the other side of the horse was tied a basket for last-minute things.

156

"Here's the fire kettle, Molly," called her mother. "Put it into the basket. Don't let it get upset."

There were red coals buried in ashes in the little iron kettle. It would be easier to light a fire with the coals than to have to strike a spark with the flint and steel. After the long day on the trail everyone would be tired and hungry.

"Don't forget the gourd filled with salt," called Mother.

No indeed, don't forget the precious salt! Salt was hard to get in the wilderness. The men had to travel many miles to reach the salt springs. They boiled away the water and left the salt. One of the pack horses carried a huge iron kettle for boiling salt water.

Molly ran back and forth. The furniture was to be left behind. Father and big brother Jed could make new furniture with their axes. The spinning wheels were tied on a horse. The loom was too heavy to take. A new one could be made.

The cabin seemed very little and lonely.

"Good-by, little house," called Molly softly.

A tiny field mouse ran across the floor. It had already moved in.

"Good-by, little mouse," laughed Molly.

Jed and Johnny were to drive the cow and the sheep. A merry time they had! The cow became frightened by all the strange noises. She ran into the woods. The boys ran after her. The sheep went in the other direction.

"I'm glad we are not taking a pig," said Mother.

At last they were off. The cow mooed. The sheep baaed, but the boys drove them down the trail.

They were starting! Molly looked back at the little cabin and waved good-by. She was sorry to leave it, but Johnny was glad. He wanted to see buffaloes and wildcats and Indians.

The next day the Harris family joined other families. The long line of people and animals grew longer. That night they camped by a river. The smell of cooking filled the air. People visited with old friends and made new ones. The children shouted and played.

But as day after day went by, people grew too tired to talk. The trail became rougher and steeper. The men tugged rocks out of the way of the horses and chopped away trees that had fallen across the trail. The mountains rose before them.

At the end of the day people were so tired that they made camp quickly and quietly. Then they dropped to the ground to rest. When they had eaten they fell asleep.

Jed and Johnny cut their feet on the rocks. Their new shoes were soon nearly torn to pieces. They had to go barefoot to save them. In the evening, by the campfire, Mother sewed deerskin moccasins for them to wear.

Then one night Molly woke to hear a shrill cry. Her father jumped to his feet. He fired his gun. Then all was quiet. But in the morning some sheep were gone. There was the track of a wildcat in the soft earth.

"Wildcats are the worst beasts of all!" said her father. "They are fierce and they are tricky. Don't ever stop to talk to a wildcat! If you see one, run!"

The cow was thin and tired, but it still gave milk for Susan. Jed milked it each night when they made camp.

"Will we ever get over the mountains?" sighed Molly.

160

Chapter 3. THE CAMP

For three weeks the horses climbed rough trails, crossed valleys and rivers. Mountains rose on either side of them. On and on and on the people went. At last they passed between the last mountains. At last they started down to Kentucky.

There were many miles still to go. There were many streams to cross.

"Watch out!" shouted one of the men.

Jed was leading a horse across a stream. Suddenly it slipped on a wet stone. It became frightened. It reared into the air. The heavy pack slipped. The rope broke. Blankets and bags of food fell into the water.

161

"Hold on to the horse!" shouted Jed's father.

If the horse started running over the rocks, it would break a leg! Then there would be nothing to do but shoot the poor beast. That would be dreadful.

The horse rolled its eyes in fright, and splashed about. But the men got to its head. They quieted the frightened animal and led it through the shallow water to safety.

Johnny and Jed pulled the pack from the water. It was wet and heavy. The women spread out blankets and opened bags of corn to dry.

"We had best camp here for the night," the men said. "It's early, but we need rest."

Men chopped down young trees to make huts for the night. A guard was set to watch the camp. Extra guns were left ready in case of need. Then some of the men went into the woods to hunt for deer or turkey. Food was needed for the weary travelers.

Molly sat under a big tree and played with the baby. She brushed away mosquitoes from the baby's face with a branch. She tickled the small Susan with the tip of the branch and made her laugh.

Then Molly smoothed out the skirt of her journey dress. It had been wet many times. It was faded and it had already been patched, but it was still a pretty color.

162

Susan grew sleepy, and Molly folded a cloak for her pillow. As she sat beside her, Molly thought of the old home. How far away it seemed! She thought of the new home and wondered what it would be like.

Suddenly a bit of bark fell off a branch above her head. Quickly Molly glanced up. Her heart gave a great jump. She wanted to scream, but she knew better. She sat perfectly still. She was thinking as hard as she could, trying to decide what she should do.

A wildcat crouched on the branch above!

Just then Molly saw Johnny coming down the path. She did not dare move or call out for fear the wildcat would leap onto the baby. Then she gave a low cry like the cry of an owl. It was a call that she and Johnny often used.

Johnny stopped and looked toward her. Slowly she raised her hand and pointed to the branch. A quick look showed Johnny what was there. He was a pioneer boy. His eyes were keen. He saw at once that it was a wildcat.

Johnny moved as quietly as an Indian. He picked one of the guns that stood ready in case of need. It was loaded. He crept silently down the path toward the tree. He aimed the gun at the wildcat.

Molly did not dare breathe. She sat as still as she could. Her eyes were on Susan. The baby was sleeping as peacefully as if she were in her own cradle at home.

Suddenly Johnny fired. The shot rang out through the woods. Susan woke up with a cry, and Molly snatched her in her arms. There was a fierce snarl from the tree. Then there was a heavy thud on the ground.

Men came running from every direction. Women came running. What had happened? Indians? Then they saw the big wildcat lying on the ground.

"It's the biggest one I ever saw!" said one man.

"It will make a fine skin for you, Johnny," said another.

But Johnny's father looked at the dead animal carefully.

"That was a good shot, son," he said. "I guess you have earned a gun of your own."

Johnny's heart gave a leap of happiness. He was to have a gun of his own!

It was two weeks later that the great news came. The fort at the end of the trail was in sight. People hurried along. Shots rang out to tell the people in the fort that a new band of pioneers was arriving.

The big gates of the fort swung open. In went people and horses and cows. The cows mooed at the scent of other cattle. People laughed and cried and talked all at once.

There was an empty cabin inside the fort. The Harris family could live there until they built a home of their own. Soon, Molly was helping her mother build a fire. Susan was crawling on the floor. The kettle was boiling.

Over the door was nailed a pair of deer horns. They were to hold the guns. They were over the door so that the guns could be snatched down quickly, in case of need.

Johnny stood looking at the horns. Molly stopped what she was doing to stand beside him.

"I'm going to put my gun there," said Johnny proudly.

He had a gun of his own! He placed it beside his father's.

Then Johnny added, "I'm going to dress the wildcat skin. It will make a fine cover for your bed this winter."

Molly's eyes gleamed. She clapped her hands with delight. Then she held out the skirt of the journey

166

dress. Father took up his fiddle. In another minute he was playing, and she and Johnny were dancing about the room.

The long trip and the hardships were forgotten. They had a home again.

So a new home was started in the wilderness. Trees were cut down. Corn was planted among the stumps. Molly helped Johnny plant the corn.

What would the pioneers have done without the Indian corn! It would grow in rough ground where wheat would not grow. The ground did not need to be plowed for corn. It was enough to dig a hole with a pointed stick and drop the seed into it.

The Indians' corn was a great gift to the pioneers.

167

HOW THE PIONEERS MADE CLOTH

1.

2.

First the sheep were sheared. The thick wool was cut off. The sheep looked silly and bare, but new wool soon grew.

Then the thick, heavy wool had to be washed. Grease had to be washed out. Sticks and burrs had to be picked out.

3.

4.

Next the wool was carded. The cards were boards with sharp nails sticking out from them. The nails pulled the wool apart and combed it.

When the wool was carded, it was soft and fluffy. Next it had to be spun into yarn. Round and round went the big spinning wheel.

5.

Then the yarn was wound on a clock reel. The dye was made in the big dye kettle. Brown dye was made from the bark of hickory trees.

6.

The wool was dipped into the dye. Then it was hung up to dry. At last, it was ready to knit into stockings, or to weave into cloth.

7.

Cloth was woven on a loom. Linen thread and woolen yarn were woven together to make linsey-woolsey cloth. It was stout and strong. Clothes must be warm for winter.

8.

When the cloth was done, then came the question, "Who needed it most?" Mary needed a dress. Father needed shirts. There was never enough to go round.

Things to Talk About

1. When the pioneers started going west to Kentucky they had to go over mountains and through mountain passes. Ask your teacher the name of those mountains. See how mountains are marked on a map.

2. Why do you think the trail over the mountains and through the mountains was called the Wilderness Trail?

3. What was the name of the man who marked out the Wilderness Trail?

4. Do you know how trails are marked through the woods? Have you ever followed a trail in the woods?

5. What things do you think a man would have to have with him to keep alive for many days in the woods?

6. Tell how Molly got her journey dress.

7. Tell how Johnny got his suit.

Things to Do

1. Make a small loom out of a box and weave a little striped rug.

2. Draw a picture to show something that happened in this story. Hold it up and choose someone to tell what the scene is.

3. What two letters are the same in all these words?

suddenly	perfectly	quietly
quickly	peacefully	slowly

Find the sentences on pages 163 and 164 that have these words in them. Be ready to read them aloud.

4. What things can you see that are made of leather?

5. Draw a picture or bring in a picture to show a spinning wheel.

6. Explain the short words in these long words.

   wildcat   shoemaker   homespun

7. Which of these words tell what the Wilderness Trail was like?

   rough   rocky   smooth   forests
   wild   easy   lonely   streams

Things to Find Out

1. Read page 157. What did Mother tell Molly to put in the basket? What did Mother tell Molly not to forget? Why were these things important?

2. Find the word on page 169 that tells what the cloth that was part wool and part linen was called.

3. Look on page 164.

   Who gave a low cry like the cry of an owl?
   Who gave a fierce snarl?
   What made the heavy thud?

4. Read page 167. Why was corn so much more useful to the pioneers than wheat? Who first gave corn to the pioneers?

5. Johnny's cap was a raccoon cap, made from the skin of a raccoon. Find out something about raccoons. Did you ever see one? Try to find a picture of one.

8

Going West by Water

A STORY OF PIONEERS ON THE OHIO RIVER

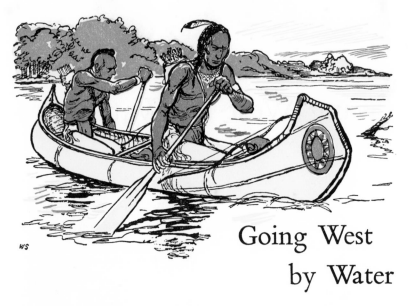

Going West
by Water

Some pioneers went west by water. They built flatboats and loaded all their things on them. The river carried the flatboats along. Downstream they floated.

But even floating downstream was dangerous. Some boats ran against rocks and were broken to pieces.

Sometimes there were dead trees stuck in the river. These dead trees could tear a hole in the bottom of a boat. Sand bars lay hidden just under the water. A boat could be stuck on a sand bar. Indians might paddle out from shore and attack.

As time went by, the Indians became more fierce and angry. They saw that the white men were taking more and more of their land. The white men were

174

killing the deer and buffaloes. They were cutting and burning down the forests. They were taking away the red men's food and homes.

Some of the white men were fair and honest. They paid the Indians for the land. They went among the red men and learned their ways. They treated them as brothers.

But other white men were greedy. They broke their promises. They stole from the red men, and burned their villages and killed their wives and children. Many Indians began to hate all white men.

It was sad that the wisest white men and the wisest Indians did not meet to decide where the white men should live and where the red men should live. It was sad that the white men did not keep their promises to the Indians.

The Ohio River is a wide, deep river that flows west through our land. Many thousands of pioneers went down the Ohio River in flatboats.

Little towns were started along the river. In these towns people could buy what they needed for the trip. Families with horses and cows and food were loaded onto big flatboats. Off the boats floated.

What was it like going west on the Ohio River? The next story will tell you.

The O'Neil Family
Goes West

Chapter 1. THE O'NEIL FAMILY

There were eight children in the O'Neil family. They went all the way from big brother Joe who was six feet tall, down to Baby Betsy who was only as big as a minute.

The O'Neils were going west. Mother gave a sigh. Again she was packing up the quilts and the blankets, the kettles and the frying pans, the spinning wheels and the churn. Father had his guns and ax, his box of tools and shovel and hoe, and his seed corn.

It was the third time that the family had moved west. When the children sat by the fire in the evening, Mother used to tell about the moves.

176

"I was born back East in Boston," Mother would begin. "That's a fine town. It has fine houses and stores and inns and more people than you could count. When I married, we went to a farm in Connecticut. I made my first journey by sleigh, for it was winter. It was fun, dashing over the snow with a pair of fast horses.

"We put hot bricks in the bottom of the sleigh to keep our feet warm. We carried along a big chunk of bean porridge all cooked and frozen stiff. We would break off a piece to eat. You know the rhyme,

Bean porridge hot, bean porridge cold,
Bean porridge in the pot, nine days old!"

Mother stopped to turn the heel on the sock that she was knitting. The children listened with eyes wide open. Cities! Farms! Sleighs! They had been brought up in the woods. But back East there were cities and towns and roads. Mother had seen them.

On went the story. "But your father was restless. He said there were too many people in Connecticut. So we moved into New York State. This time we went by stagecoach.

"Oh, a stagecoach is a fine way to travel! But sometimes the stagecoach got stuck. Once it almost turned over. I let out such a scream that everyone thought I was killed. Joe was just a baby then."

The children looked at big brother Joe, six feet tall. It was funny to think of him as a baby, riding in a stagecoach.

"Finally we reached our next home," said Mother. "It was wild country, all woods and Indians. But pretty soon your father began talking about moving again, this time into Pennsylvania. That was even wilder than the country we had left behind. Not a road to drive on, or an inn to stay at. No more stagecoaches!

"We started out in an oxcart pulled by six oxen. Sometimes the trail was so narrow that your father had to chop down trees to get the cart through. The cart could be heard five miles off, banging over rocks. It was lonely in the forest at night. A bear stole my bacon. Wolves howled."

Mother stopped again to count the stitches in her knitting. Then she said slowly, "Now we are moving again, this time into Indiana. We are going down the Ohio River in a flatboat."

Mother gave a sigh. "Each time I leave a place I always take a root from my rose bush and my lilac bush with me in a pot," she said. "The first ones came from my old home in Boston. Everywhere I've lived I have had roses and lilacs. I always was a great one for flowers."

178

Each older O'Neil child had a younger one to care for on the journey. Eight-year-old Mary Jane had charge of Davy, who was two. He kept her busy. Now he was falling headfirst into the flatboat that was to carry them down the Ohio River.

Mary Jane grabbed Davy by the back of his homespun dress. Then she helped her older sister Martha carry Baby Betsy down.

Mary Jane peeked into the cabin of the boat. "It's just like a playhouse!" she cried.

But it was far from being a playhouse! The walls were of thick planks. The windows were narrow slits. It was a fort as well as a house. No bullets or arrows could go through those thick walls.

The girls spread out gay quilts and blankets. They unpacked pewter dishes and wooden bowls.

There came a great noise from the deck. They ran out to see what was happening. The boys were driving the horses and mules, the cows and pigs and sheep aboard. One of the pigs got away and the boys had to chase him.

Suddenly Mary Jane saw a strange old man standing by the boat. He was dressed in rags. His hair and beard were long.

"You had better not talk to him," whispered Martha. "He looks queer."

But the old man smiled at Mary Jane. He smiled in a way that made her forget that she was afraid. She smiled back.

"Here is something for you, little girl," he said, and he gave her a little bag.

"There are seeds in there," said the old man. "Apple seeds. Plant them by your new home, and someday you will have fine young trees. Every child should have apple trees to climb and apples to eat."

"Thank you," said Mary Jane. "Thank you very much."

She ran to her mother with the seeds.

"That's a fine idea!" said her mother. "It was kind of the old man. He must be Johnny Appleseed. He goes about giving people seeds, and tending young trees so the new places won't seem so lonely. I wish I had an extra rose bush to give him."

"He was poor and ragged," said Mary Jane.

"Don't judge people by their looks," said her mother. "He spends his time and money doing kind things for people. There are plenty of people that bless his name."

Mary Jane looked at the little brown seeds. They were more than apple seeds, she thought. They were seeds of kindness. It would be fine to have apple trees by the new home.

180

Chapter 2. ON THE OHIO

The next day the O'Neil family started off. There were three other men on board. One man had his wife and baby. The boat was well filled with people and animals. It was like a floating farm. Out into the broad river it floated quietly.

One man stood on the roof of the cabin and steered with a long oar. The boys and men took turns steering. The women cooked and knitted and washed and cared for the babies. There was time for talking and fun as well.

When the boat floated past log houses, the children waved to the people ashore. But sometimes day after day went by with no sign of people or houses. The woods came down to the water on either side. It was fall, and the leaves were turning red and gold.

Mary Jane liked best of all to have one of the men take out his fiddle. Then they would all sing and dance. She would beg for "Old Dan Tucker," and they would sing:

> "Old Dan Tucker was a fine old man.
> He washed his face with a frying pan.
> He combed his hair with a wagon wheel.
> And died with a toothache in his heel!"

182

One night, as they sat on deck, singing and laughing, a light flamed in the sky ahead.

"Is it a forest fire?" asked Joe.

"I don't think it is," said his father slowly. Then he added, "I don't like the looks of it."

In less time than it takes to tell, the lanterns on board were put out. The little children were hurriedly tucked away in the bunks. Men stood at the window slits with their guns. They watched the light ahead.

Mary Jane could see the light from a window. There were clouds over the stars. No moon shone.

In the darkness of the night the heavy boat floated on and on. For there is no way to stop a flatboat except to run it ashore. And there is no way to hurry a flatboat. It floats slowly or fast, as the river runs.

Brother Joe stood at the steering oar.

"Keep as near the bank as you dare," said his father in a low voice. "Steer close to the far shore. But watch out! Don't get us stuck on a sand bar!"

The heavy dark boat swung round the curve in the river. Suddenly strange sounds filled the air. Shouts and yells rang across the water. It was easy to see where the sounds came from. A huge fire burned near the bank of the river. Dark figures danced about it.

"Indians!" whispered Mr. O'Neil. "It's a war dance!"

The fire made a path of light across the dark water. Slowly but steadily the flatboat floated toward the light.

Mother leaned over Mary Jane and whispered to her, "Keep Davy quiet. If Father calls, wrap Davy in a quilt and bring him out on deck. Be ready to do just what Father says, and don't make a sound!"

Nearer and nearer to the light floated the flatboat. The cries and shouts of the dancers grew louder and louder. The warriors leaped around the fire and waved war clubs in the air. Boom, boom, boom, went the beat of the big war drums. It seemed to Mary Jane as though her heart was beating as fiercely as the drums.

Would the Indians see the boat as it floated quietly past? Would the darkness hide it?

"No one is to fire a gun unless I give the word," whispered Mr. O'Neil.

184

Baby Betsy turned in her sleep and gave a little cry. Martha bent over her. She sang softly to her. The baby gave a sigh and was quiet.

Mary Jane sat by Davy. He was asleep now. She thought of Joe on the roof of the cabin steering the boat. Oh, if only he could push the boat along faster with that big oar! Oh, how she wished he could push them past the light and into the darkness beyond!

The Indians were busy with their dance. The chief was telling how the white men had taken their hunting grounds and killed their deer. He was telling how they had burned the forests. As he spoke, the warriors stopped to listen. Then the wild dance began again.

On and on floated the silent boat. Then slowly it floated into the light from the fire. But the Indians were so busy with their dance that they did not see it. Suddenly one Indian looked toward the water.

185

The Indian gave a great shout. The drums stopped. Dark figures came leaping down the bank of the river. Arrows flew through the air. Canoes were pushed into the water.

"No one is to shoot unless an Indian gets close enough to climb on board," ordered Mr. O'Neil firmly.

Bullets hit the flatboat too. The Indians had bought guns from the white men. Some had guns now as well as bows and arrows. But the bullets did not pierce the thick sides of the boat.

On and on the flatboat floated, into the safe darkness of the night. At last the Indian canoes turned back. The cries grew fainter. Then the drums began again.

It was then that Mary Jane found that she wanted to cry. She threw herself into her mother's arms.

"Cry all you want to now, dearie," said her mother. "You were quiet and brave when there was danger. That's the important thing!"

Just then something happened that made Mary Jane forget herself. The men came in carrying brother Joe. A bullet had hit him. He had been shot as he stood at the steering oar. He had not cried out. His cries would have told the Indians where the boat was. He had stood bravely at his work till the danger was past.

Chapter 3. THE NEW HOME

Everyone was glad when the new home was reached.

Joe was better, but he still lay white and quiet in his bunk. Mary Jane ran in and out of the cabin to bring him the news. The flatboat was tied up at the shore near a little town of log houses. Father had bought land. The men were starting to build a log cabin.

It took a week to build the new log house. The three men who had come down the river with the O'Neils paid for the trip by helping. Seventy or eighty straight tall pine trees were cut. The trunks were sawed to the right length. The ends were cut so that they fitted together. It was hard, heavy work, but the log walls were thick and strong. No bullet or arrow could go through them. Winter wind and snow could not get in, for the cracks were filled with clay and mud.

At last Mary Jane ran to the flatboat to tell Joe the news. The house was done. The front door was hung on leather hinges. A wooden latch held it shut.

The furniture was soon made. The table was a rough slab of wood set on four posts. The posts fitted into holes bored in the floor. Short posts held up the rough beds. Ropes were stretched across to hold the bags of hay that were used for mattresses. Bear skins and blankets were spread over them.

It was an exciting day when the O'Neil family moved into the new house. Mother cooked bear meat over the open fire. Martha made "hasty pudding" of corn meal. It was called "hasty pudding" because it could be made so fast. The corn meal was boiled in water. Then molasses was poured over it.

The flatboat was taken to pieces. It was too heavy to push back up the river. The planks would make a fine barn for the animals.

"The girls ought to go to school this winter," said Mr. O'Neil, as they sat down to the first dinner. "I need the boys to cut trees and split rails for fences. But the girls can have some schooling. There is a school started in the town."

188

Martha and Mary Jane looked at each other in surprise. A school! They had never been to school! They could read. Mother had taught them to read from the Bible. They could write their names, but that was all. What would it be like at school?

The next day the girls took Davy and walked past the open door of the school. They peeked in. The schoolhouse was a log cabin. The children sat on benches with no backs. The schoolteacher sat at a high desk. On his desk he had a big pen made from a feather. He looked very solemn.

The youngest children stood in front of him. They were reading.

"A, b, ab," said one child slowly. "E, b, eb."

It did not sound interesting to Mary Jane. Then one boy at the back of the room pinched another boy. The schoolmaster shouted at him, and rapped on his desk with a cane. Mary Jane gave a jump and Davy began to cry. The girls hurried home.

"Couldn't we wait till next year to begin school?" they begged.

"I'll help with the spinning," said Martha.

"I'll help with the soap making and the candle dipping," said Mary Jane.

"I'll help churn the butter," said Martha.

"I'll pound the corn into meal and bake the bread," said Mary Jane.

"Well, well," laughed Mother. "I really don't see how I could get along without you! You can wait until next year if you will read from the Bible to me every night and sew on your samplers every day."

So every day, when the housework was done, the girls sewed on their samplers. Every evening they sat by the open fire and read to their mother.

How warm and bright and comforting that fire was! The back log was so big that a horse had to drag it into the kitchen. Then Joe and his father rolled it into the fireplace.

Sometimes the big back log burned for weeks. Mother piled smaller wood on top of it. How warm

190

and comforting the fire was! It was good to sit by the fire after the long day's work.

There was so much to be done!

"I wish we each had three pairs of hands," said Father.

All winter the boys and men worked. They cut down trees to build fences so that the cows would not stray into the woods and be killed by the wolves and bears. They cleared land to plant in the spring.

When warm weather came at last, the planting of corn and wheat and oats began. Mother and the girls started a garden. Beans and potatoes were started.

"I hope the bears don't eat the ears of corn, and the deer don't eat everything else!" sighed Mother.

She planted her rose and lilac bushes by the cabin door.

"I want to plant my apple seeds," said Mary Jane.

Father found a good place and dug up the ground for her. Mary Jane planted the seeds in a row. Then she built a fence around them to keep out the chickens. She watched for the tiny shoots to come up.

"If Johnny Appleseed ever comes this way," said Mary Jane, "he'll be pleased with my apple trees."

"It will be a long time before those bear fruit," said Martha.

"I can wait," said Mary Jane.

WHAT PIONEER SCHOOLS WERE LIKE

1.

2.

The schoolhouse was a log cabin with a fireplace to heat it. The children who sat near the fire in winter were too hot. The others were too cold.

The smallest children learned from a horn book. It was a board with large and small letters pasted on. A thin sheet of cow's horn kept it clean.

3.

4.

After the horn book, the children read the New England Primer. This is a page from the New England Primer.

Next came the spelling book. Every school had spelling matches. Even grown-ups had spelling matches.

5.

A pen knife

Quill

Sand   Inkwell

Children wrote with quill pens made from feathers. The teacher cut the ends of the quill with a sharp knife. It was called a pen knife.

6.

Paper was hard to get, so most of the work was done on slates. Slates were thin sheets of stone. They could be washed. Slate pencils often squeaked.

7.

A sampler

Little girls often learned their letters by sewing them on samplers. This is a picture of a sampler.

8.

The teacher always had a paddle for naughty children. Any child who would not learn sat in the corner.

Things to Talk About

1. Do you think it was easier for pioneers to go west by land or by water? Why?

2. Why were the Indians becoming more fierce and angry? What do we wish the wisest Indians and the wisest white men had done? Does it ever happen today that we need to have wise people meet to try to make things go well? Does it happen at school?

3. Read page 176. What did Mother take west with her? What did Father take? Make a list of these things on the blackboard. Which three things do you think were the most important? Why? Take a class vote to see which three things you think were most needed.

4. Mr. O'Neil said, "I wish we each had three pairs of hands." Why do you think he felt that way?

5. What is pewter? Why would dishes of pewter or wood be better than china for the pioneers?

Things to Do

1. Find the Ohio River on the map. Into what river does it flow?

2. Arrange a bulletin board with pictures of different ways of traveling.

3. Arrange an exhibit of toys that show different ways of traveling.

4. Bring a feather to school. Ask your teacher to cut the end in a point. Let each member of the class sign his name in ink with it.

5. Mother had moved from Connecticut to New York State, then on to Pennsylvania and out to Indiana. Find those states on the map. Have you seen cars with license plates from them?

6. What part of these words is the same?

      unpack   unload   untie   undo

What do you think that *un* in front of a word means? Can you put *un* in front of these words?

      lock   finished   happy   interesting

7. Which of these words have the same endings?

| restless | careless | fearless |
| happiness | kindness | darkness |

Use some of these words in the sentences below.

Father was _____ and wanted to move again.
People spoke of Johnny Appleseed's _____.
Never be _____ with fire.
The boat floated on into the ————.

Things to Find Out

1. Look on page 188 and find out how the furniture for the new house was made.

2. Look on page 190. Make a list of the things the girls offered to do to help. What do you do at home to help?

3. Look on page 191. Make a list of the things that the O'Neils planted. What did Molly plant?

4. Study pages 192 and 193. Be ready to tell all you can about a pioneer school.

9

Going West
by Wagon Train

A STORY OF PIONEERS TRAVELING
BY COVERED WAGON

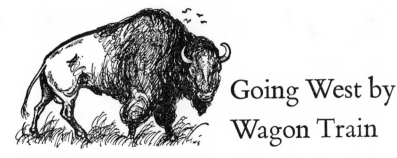

Going West by Wagon Train

West, west, west, went the pioneers. They crossed the Mississippi River in boats. They came to the wide prairie where the buffaloes lived. Some pioneers made their homes there. Other pioneers kept on.

After the prairies were crossed, there came the plains. Then, far ahead, rose great mountains. First came the Rocky Mountains. Then, for a thousand miles, there were deserts and mountains to be crossed.

In many places, the trails through the mountains were steep and dangerous. In summer, as well as in winter, there was snow on the white peaks. Storms blew down the trails.

In the desert, the sun beat down. Often there was no water or grass. Many oxen and mules died.

People threw away things to make wagons lighter. Piles of furniture, stoves, trunks, cooking things, and food were left behind. There was nothing else to do.

The way was marked by graves of people who had died. Still the pioneers struggled on.

198

Many pioneers traveled in covered wagons. These wagons were painted blue with red trimming. The ends were higher than the middle part so that babies and bundles would not fall out. The wagons could bump over rocks and down into mud holes.

If rivers were too deep to wade across, the wheels of the wagon were taken off. The wagon box was like a boat. It was rowed across the water, or pulled by ropes. The animals swam.

It was a gay sight to see a long line of covered wagons starting out from the old French city of St. Louis. The line was called a wagon train. It was safer to travel in a wagon train than alone. Sometimes two or three hundred wagons set out together. Twenty miles was a good day's trip.

It was not so gay a sight as the weeks went by. Colors faded in the sun and wind. Wheels were broken on rocks. People and wagons were worn and battered.

Sometimes men struggled for hours to drag one wagon after another up a steep cliff. Sometimes it took fifteen oxen to pull each wagon across a stream.

Sometimes Indians attacked, but at other times Indians helped. They saved many lives. They led to safety many parties of pioneers who were lost.

What was it like, going west in a covered wagon? The next story will tell you.

"Catch Up! Catch Up!"

Chapter 1. THE WIDE PRAIRIE

By four o'clock in the morning everyone was up.

Dogs barked. Cows mooed. Babies cried. Women called to the children. Men shouted at oxen and horses. They had turned the animals loose to graze for an hour before starting.

A hundred wagons stood in a huge circle. Inside the circle, the women were building fires and cooking food. By sunrise, the wagon train must be ready to start.

200

"Hurry up, Dan!" called his sister. "Finish your breakfast fast! Pack the dishes for me."

"Hurry up, Dan!" cried his father. "Help me with these oxen!"

"Hurry up, Dan!" called his mother. "Lift this tent into the wagon!"

Dan gave a groan. All was hurry and noise. It was always this way the first thing in the morning. Everybody wanted him to do everything at once.

Soon would come the call, "Catch up! Catch up!" At that call, the first wagon would start out. The second and third would fall into line.

But today was to be different.

As Dan sat eating his breakfast, he felt the ground shake under him. He put his ear down to listen.

"I hear something coming," he called to his father.

His father bent over to listen. Thud, thud, thud, came the sound of heavy hoofs on the earth.

"Indians?" asked Dan.

"Too loud," said his father. "It sounds more like buffaloes."

He called quickly to some men. They saddled their horses and rode off. Dan jumped on a horse, and followed his father. They galloped to a low hill. They stopped and looked out over miles and miles of rolling prairie.

Far away Dan could see a cloud of dust moving toward them. Nearer and nearer it came. At last he could make out a mass of buffaloes. They came thundering across the prairie toward the camp. Something had frightened them.

"We must keep them away from the wagons," shouted Dan's father. A herd of buffaloes could wreck a whole camp.

The men spread out across the prairie. They must drive the herd in another direction. The horses were excited and nervous.

"Keep close to me, Dan," shouted his father.

On and on came the herd. The ground shook under the beat of their hoofs. But the buffaloes were stupid animals. They seemed to pay little attention where they went.

One man rode forward. Suddenly a big buffalo saw him. The buffalo stopped and looked. It was curious about this stranger. Dan could see the small horns sticking out. He could see the small red eyes.

The man fired. There came a roar from the buffalo. The beast was wounded. It stamped the ground with its sharp hoofs. Its long tongue hung from its mouth. Then, with a roar, it dashed forward. Straight toward Dan, the buffalo came!

203

For a second, Dan's horse stood still, trembling. The buffalo was almost upon them. Then the horse gave a quick jump to one side. Dan almost went over its head. He clung to its neck. The buffalo went dashing past. Dan's horse galloped to safety.

Another man aimed his heavy gun and fired. The buffalo fell to the ground. It was dead.

Dan slipped back into his saddle. Then he quieted his frightened horse. That jump had saved his life. He patted the horse's neck.

A second and a third buffalo were killed. Then the herd turned. It galloped off in another direction. Away from the wagons it went. The camp was safe. For a while the men followed the herd. They killed as many buffaloes as they could.

It was noon when the party got back to camp. The sun was hot. Dan was tired, but there was no rest in camp. The mules and oxen had been filled with terror at the noise. They had broken loose. They had scattered far and wide across the prairie.

"It will be work, rounding them up," said Dan's father. "We had best stay right here for a few days. It's a good time to dry buffalo meat to take with us."

All that afternoon and the next day, Dan and the boys rode across the prairie. They hunted for lost oxen and they tried to catch runaway mules. In some

204

places the buffalo grass grew as tall as a horse's back. Here and there, patches of sunflowers bloomed. Prairie dogs sat up on their hind legs and barked at the boys. Dan rode near them, but they dived down into their holes.

Some of the men cut up the buffalo meat. They hung it in the sun to dry. It was well to have dried meat on hand.

Three days later, the cry "Catch up! Catch up!" came again. All but three of the lost animals had been found. The train was ready to start.

At sunrise, the barking and shouting and mooing and the creaking of wagon wheels began. Tents were down. Kettles and frying pans were packed. Bedding and buffalo robes were rolled up.

Slowly the long line of wagons moved across the prairie. It looked like a long line of crawling ants. Dust filled the air. Dan and his father walked by the side of the wagon. His mother and sister rode. The day's march had begun.

Chapter 2. MOUNTAINS AND DESERT

Little by little, the trail began to rise. The rich prairie land was left behind. Ahead, mountains showed against the sky. The trail became so rough that the wagons bumped and groaned.

Every night there were wagon wheels to mend. Iron rims were made tight by hammering in wooden wedges. The rough going was pounding the wheels to bits. When an ox died, its skin was used to make strong straps to tie up weak wheels.

"Watch out for rattlesnakes," warned Dan's father as they made camp at night.

Wolves and coyotes howled around the wagons. The stars were bright and beautiful. Dan lay and looked up at them.

One evening, Dan and his father rode away from camp looking for game. Fresh meat would taste good. They rode up a strange, wild valley. Dan watched eagerly for any sign of game. Perhaps he would see a deer.

Suddenly he saw something that made him stop his horse. Ahead was a large covered wagon. It was tipped sideways. One wheel was broken. In front of it lay two dead oxen. Big black birds whirled in the air above it.

Dan looked at his father. They had seen many broken-down wagons along the way. They had seen many oxen and mules and horses that had died on the long, hard trail. But this wagon looked so lonely and so helpless!

Dan's father fired at the birds to frighten them away. They were fierce and greedy. They flapped their great wings and flew away. Dan and his father rode toward the wagon.

They called and they shouted. There was no answer. The horses did not like the sight. They rolled their eyes and tried to turn back.

"I don't believe there's anyone there, but you'd better see," called Dan's father.

Clothes, bedding, and kettles had tumbled out of the wagon as it tipped. The oxen had dragged it after them as they looked for water. They had gone as far as they could before they dropped to the ground.

"Somebody has had a mighty hard time," said Dan.

His father looked very sober. With bad luck this might happen to any of them.

Just then Dan heard a strange sound. Was it an animal or a bird? A little sobbing sound came from the wagon. Dan jumped from his horse.

"Go carefully there," his father warned him.

Dan crept up to the wagon. Then he climbed up on the big wheel and peeked under the cover. The little cry came again.

"There's somebody in here," he shouted.

There in a basket lay a baby girl. She was very thin. She was sobbing softly. Dan picked her up and climbed out of the wagon. She clung to him.

His father looked down at the baby.

"Well, this is a pretty funny hunt we came on," he said. "I didn't know we were baby hunting. Wrap her up in something."

Dan pulled a small quilt from the wagon. Then he held the baby up. His father took her gently.

"Poor little thing," he said. "Her father and mother must have left the wagon to look for help. Wonder what happened to them. Shot by Indians perhaps. Another day and this baby would have been dead. Lucky we came along!"

When they reached camp, the women crowded around to see the baby. She was dressed in a neat linsey-woolsey dress of dark blue. She had on a little blue-and-white checked apron. Dan's mother heated milk for her. She fed the tiny girl a drop at a time. Dan's sister held her.

The next morning the men rode back to the broken-down wagon. They hunted and they looked. No sign of the people could they find.

"I'll keep the baby," said Dan's mother. "I've been wanting a baby."

It was surprising how fast the baby gained. In a few days she grew stronger. She laughed and smiled when Dan came near. She was warm. She was loved. She knew nothing of what had happened.

Chapter 3. THE LOST TRAIL

Dan woke one morning to find everything white. His buffalo robe was frozen to the ground. He was stiff and cold.

"We can't go on today," said his father in an anxious voice. "We might lose the trail."

Lose the trail! Those were words that filled every pioneer's heart with fear.

Getting a fire started was hard. Dan crawled under a wagon to find a dry spot. His hands ached with the cold. At last he got a small fire going.

It was good to smell the wood smoke. His mother cooked hasty pudding. She warmed milk for the baby.

All that day, people lay inside tents and wagons trying to keep warm. They wrapped buffalo robes about themselves. It was hard to keep the children quiet. The dogs howled. Every now and then came the call of a wolf. All day snow and rain fell.

Next morning the men gathered together. They looked at the sky and they talked. The snow had stopped, but the sky was gray. The men were anxious and troubled. Could they find the trail with the snow on the ground? At last the word was given for the wagon train to start.

210

It was a quiet starting this time, but it was good to have something to do. Dan hurried to help. He did not have to be called.

A party of men rode on ahead to be sure of the trail. Dan's father led them.

"You drive the oxen, Dan," he called.

Dan took the long whip and led the beasts. They moved along slowly. The oxen slipped on the wet rocks.

Then one wagon ahead broke down. A wheel was gone. The men hurried forward and pulled it out of the way. The wagon would have to be left. A few things could be saved and piled into another wagon. The rest must be left behind.

The woman and the children from the broken wagon sadly moved in with friends. The man walked. The long line moved on again.

By noon the whole train stopped. It had begun to rain again. Then the men who had ridden ahead came back. They brought bad news. They spoke quietly, but their eyes looked worried and afraid.

"We've lost the trail," they said.

Lost the trail! People looked at each other in terror. What would happen now? What could they do, lost in the mountains? Who was there to help them?

212

Suddenly, out of the storm, came two men on horseback. Two tall Indians rode toward the wagons. Straight and tall they sat on their Indian ponies.

Men jumped up. They reached for their guns. Children hurried to their mothers. They watched the Indians with eyes big with fear. What were they going to do?

The leader of the Indians made a sign. It was a sign of peace. Dan's father hurried forward. He gave a great sigh of relief. He shook hands with the red men. He made them welcome.

213

There was little to offer the Indians. Dan's father led them to a dry spot by a wagon. Dan spread a buffalo robe for them to sit upon. His mother brought them food.

For some time, the Indians sat quietly eating. Dan looked at them eagerly. One must be a great chief. He wore a fine deerskin suit. He had a buffalo robe over his shoulders. Around his neck hung strings of bear claws. Both Indians had guns.

One Indian spoke a little English. When he had finished eating he took out a pipe. He filled it with tobacco. It was a peace pipe.

"Smoke," said the Indian. White man and Indian smoked the pipe of peace together.

Dan's father told the Indians of the lost trail. He asked their help.

One Indian nodded his head slowly. He spoke to the other man.

Then he said quietly, "We show trail."

They must start at once. The rain would swell the rivers. The wagons might not be able to get across. There was no time to lose.

Big wheels began to creak and groan as they started through the wet snow. But there was a different feeling inside the wagons. Instead of being frightened and lost, people were happy and excited.

214

The Indians were helping them to find the trail. The Indians knew the way. Through a narrow rocky pass the Indians led the line of wagons. The mountains rose like steep walls on either side.

"We would never have found this way," said the men in wonder. "Can we get the wagons through?"

The Indians rode on ahead. They knew these mountains. This was their home.

By evening the wagons were back on the trail. People talked and laughed as they made camp. They were cold and wet, but they were safe. They had found the trail.

Dan's father called to him. "We must give presents to the Indians," he said.

The Indians liked the white men's clothes. Dan's father chose two fine coats and hats. Then he picked out a roll of red cloth and a package of red powder to mix into paint. Was that enough? Would the Indians be pleased?

He added beads and little mirrors for them to take to the women.

Dan carried the presents to the Indians. Solemnly the red men took them. As they started to climb onto their horses, Dan stepped forward. He took out his hunting knife. He wore it always at his belt. He held it out to the Indian chief.

"This is for your son," he said.

Solemnly the chief took the knife. He put it in his belt. Then he took the long string of bear claws. He put it around Dan's neck.

"My son and you, brothers," he said.

Then the Indians rode quietly away.

1.

2.

The wagons were strong and well made. The front and back of the wagon tipped up so that no babies or bundles could fall out. Chests, boxes, chairs, and tables were loaded inside.

At night the wagons stopped in a great circle. Fires were lighted and supper cooked. Some people slept in the wagons. Others put up tents. Men guarded the camp at night.

3.

4.

In the morning the train was off by sunrise. It stretched far across the prairie. Oxen pulled most of the wagons. Herds of cows were driven behind.

When a river was crossed, a shallow place was found. It was called a ford. Into the water the oxen splashed. Down bumped the wagons.

5.

If the river was too deep to ford, the wheels were taken off. The cracks in the wagon box were filled up. The wagon was used for a boat. The animals swam.

6.

Sometimes the wagons had to be dragged up steep trails. At other times they had to be let down steep cliffs. The men tied ropes to them and let them down slowly.

7.

Sometimes Indians attacked. They stole horses, cows, and oxen. They burned the wagons. At other times Indians led the pioneers to safety.

8.

Day after day the train went on. Babies and old people rode inside. The rest of the family took turns walking and driving the animals.

Things to Talk About

1. Tell some of the adventures that pioneers going west in a covered wagon might have.

2. What did the pioneers do if they came to a river that was shallow enough to wade across? What did they do if the river was too deep to wade across? What is the difference between a ford and a Ford?

3. Why did people sometimes have to throw things away as they crossed the desert? What sort of things did they leave behind? How do you think the women felt?

4. Tell how camp was made at night.

5. Do you think that the covered wagons were well planned for hard use?

Things to Do

1. Draw pictures of covered wagons. Look on page 199 to see what colors to use.

2. Find out all you can about buffaloes. Cut out buffalo masks from large sheets of tagboard. Make up an Indian buffalo dance.

3. Draw a picture of mountains. Show where you would go to try to find a trail between the peaks. The easiest way to get through the mountains is called a *mountain pass*.

4. Make a model in plasticine and cardboard of a covered wagon going through a mountain pass.

5. Act out some scenes from the story.

220

6. Make up a story yourself of something that might have happened in a covered wagon. Choose some children to help you act it out.

7. Make a list of the animals that went west with the pioneers.

Things to Find Out

1. Find the answers to these questions. If you do not know the answers, look on page 199.

   a. What was a long line of covered wagons called?
   b. How many wagons often traveled together?
   c. Why was it better for a number of covered wagons to travel together than for one wagon to travel alone?
   d. What was a good day's trip for a covered wagon? Do you know how long it would take a car to go that far?
   e. What was the name of the city from which many of the covered wagons started?

2. Find these words in the story and explain what they mean.

   Page 200   turned the animals loose to graze
   Page 202   thundering across the prairie
   Page 203   curious about this stranger
   Page 205   like a long line of crawling ants
   Page 212   their eyes looked worried and afraid
   Page 214   there was a different feeling inside the wagons

10

Three Trails
through the Mountains

STORIES ABOUT
THE SANTA FE TRAIL, THE OREGON TRAIL,
AND THE CALIFORNIA TRAIL

Three Trails through the Mountains

In the spring, the little town of Independence in Missouri was a busy place. In the spring, the wagon trains started out from Independence on the long trails west.

Sometimes a thousand pioneers would be camped outside the little town, waiting. They must wait until the snow was off the mountain trails. Then they must start quickly, for they must be through the mountains before snow fell again.

Nearly every other shed in Independence was a blacksmith's shop. Clang, clang went hammers on red-hot iron. The wagons must be ready for the long, hard trip. The iron rims must be tight. Chains must

224

be ready. Bolts and nails must be made. Burning sparks flew into the air.

People who were lucky enough to have any money left bought last things for the trip.

"I may need another bag of flour and some coffee," cried one woman.

"I want sugar and salt pork," said another.

The men sold or traded horses and mules and oxen while they waited.

At last, word came that the trail was safe. Off the wagon trains moved. The little town of Independence settled down to quiet again.

There were three trails that went from the town of Independence. They led to very different parts of our country.

One was the Sante Fe Trail. It went southwest over the mountains and through the desert to the old city of Santa Fe. Spanish pioneers had built that city.

One was the Oregon Trail. It led northwest along the roaring Columbia River. Tall dark trees covered the sides of the mountains.

The third trail was the California Trail. It led west, across the mountains to the Pacific Ocean.

The next three stories will tell you what the pioneers found at the end of each of these three trails.

Nick's Sombrero

AT THE END OF THE SANTA FE TRAIL

Mules are best in the desert. Nick felt sure of it. They are stronger than horses. They are faster than oxen.

Sometimes mules are mean and hard to manage. Nick had to watch their heels. They were tricky. Still, mules were best.

Nick sat by his father, who was driving three pairs of black mules. The animals trotted quickly along over the dry, rough earth. There was excitement in the air.

The city of Santa Fe was near!

Six weeks before, Nick and his father had left Independence. For six weeks they had crossed mountains where they nearly froze at night. They had crossed deserts where the sun beat down and where there was no water for sixty miles. Day and night, they had kept a sharp watch for Indians. Now that was all over.

Santa Fe was near!

All the men were dressed up in their best clothes. Fine suits and shiny boots had been pulled out of dusty wagons. Nick had changed his torn overalls and faded blue shirt for fresh ones. Santa Fe was near!

The mountains rose blue and soft across the desert. Big jack rabbits dashed out from behind bushes. Wolves and coyotes sneaked past.

"Watch out there!" cried Nick.

A big rattlesnake lay on the trail. It was ready to strike. The mules jumped to one side. The heavy wheels of the wagon passed over the snake.

The wagon was full of goods to trade. There were cotton cloth and gay silks. There were tools and knives to trade for leather and furs and silver. This was the first time that Nick had come with his father. This year, Nick, too, was riding into Santa Fe.

There was one thing that troubled Nick. He had no hat. His hair stood up straight on top of his head.

Nick had lost his hat in a storm. One night thunder had roared. Lightning had flashed. Rain had poured down. Then came a wild wind. Nick had tried to hang on to the little tent where he was sleeping. The wind had blown both him and the tent away.

Luckily it had thrown them against the wheel of a wagon. Nick had hung onto the wheel till the storm passed. But his hat was gone.

"Probably blown clear back to the Missouri River," said one of the men.

It was hard not to have a hat. A hat could be used to dip water from a spring. A hat was useful to fan away the clouds of flies and mosquitoes. At night you could put it over your face to keep off the mosquitoes. Yes, hats were useful.

The sun was hot. Nick tied a red handkerchief over his head. He sighed. And now, he had to ride into Santa Fe with no hat! He had no hat to wave.

The last night in camp, the men had cut each other's hair. They had trimmed each other's whiskers. They had pulled out their best suits. They had brushed their hats. Today everyone wore a hat except Nick.

"There's Santa Fe ahead!" shouted his father.

Far ahead, Nick could see fields and trees and houses with flat roofs. A tall church rose among them.

228

Shouts and cheers came from the men. Guns were fired into the air. Hats were waved. On went the mules at a gallop. Down the last hill came the wagons at top speed.

Around the square in the middle of the town they went. Then they stopped at the old inn at the end of the trail.

"Well, my boy, we've made it!" cried Nick's father.

Nick had never seen a town like Santa Fe. The houses back in Independence were made of wood. In Santa Fe, they were made of clay and stone.

People came crowding around the wagons. The women wore full skirts of gay colors. They had high

229

combs in their black hair. They wore bright flowers.
They spoke Spanish. Nick could not understand what
they said.

The men were in white. Some wore red sashes.
They had on big wide hats. Nick looked at those hats.
Oh, how he wanted one!

"Those big hats are called 'sombreros,' " said his
father. "How would you like to ride back into
Independence with a sombrero on your head?"

There was no more time to think of hats just then.
The wagons must be unloaded.

That night the old inn was alive with laughter and sound. There was a dance. Nick and his father watched. Pretty Spanish girls whirled round and round. Then the men threw down their sombreros. The girls danced lightly around them.

You needed a hat in Santa Fe, even to dance! Nick had no hat. He went back to the wagon. He climbed inside and went to sleep.

The next morning, Nick started out early. He was going to get a hat. He did not know where. He did not know how. He had no money. But somehow he was going to get a hat.

His light hair stood on end. His blue eyes were firm. His mind was made up. He was going to get a hat. People smiled as he went by.

At the trader's, there were only big hats.

"How much?" asked Nick. He pointed to a hat.

"Too much and too big," laughed the trader.

Nick put the hat on his head. It covered him, nose and all. The men in the room began to laugh. Nick pulled the hat off. He did not like to be laughed at.

Nick walked across the square. A boy just his age was leaning against the wall. He had on a hat, a wide black hat. True, it was faded. There was a hole in it, but it was a good hat still.

Nick stopped and looked at it. It was just his size. He took the red handkerchief out of his pocket. He took a knife with a broken point. Then he found a little pocket mirror. He held them all out toward the boy. He pointed at the hat.

The boy looked surprised. He took off his hat and looked at it. He was fond of that hat. He put the hat on again. He would not trade it.

Nick flashed sunlight with the mirror. He flashed light in the eyes of a mule that stood near. The animal made a loud noise and put its lips back to bite. Nick and the boy laughed. But when Nick pointed to the hat, the boy shook his head.

There was one last thing deep in Nick's pocket. It was the most precious thing that he owned. It was his mouth organ. He could play "Home, Sweet Home," and "Yankee Doodle."

Could Nick bear to offer his mouth organ? Would the boy trade his hat for it?

Slowly and sadly, Nick put the mouth organ to his lips. He started to play "Yankee Doodle."

He played loud and clear. This might be the last tune he was ever to play. He would do his best.

The boy jumped up. His black eyes shone. He pulled the hat from his head. He held it out to Nick. He pointed to the mouth organ. He wanted it and he wanted it right away.

But Nick would not stop playing. He played through to the end of the tune. Then slowly, he started to hold out the mouth organ toward the boy.

Suddenly there was a sound behind him. Someone cried, "Bravo!" Something was clapped on Nick's head. Nick turned quickly. There stood his father.

"I've been hunting all over town for you," said his father. "Never would have found you if it hadn't been for that music."

Back into Nick's pocket dropped the mouth organ.

234

His hands went to his head.

"How's that for a fit?" laughed his father.

Nick felt something large and round and smooth. It was a hat. It was a sombrero. It was just the right size for him.

The boy watched sadly. The mouth organ was safe in Nick's pocket. The boy put his old hat back on his head. He leaned back against the wall. Oh well, some day he'd have a mouth organ, too.

Nick waved good-by. Then out came the organ. As he followed his father, Nick played for all the world to hear.

> Yankee Doodle came to town
> Riding on a pony,
> Stuck a feather in his hat
> And called it Macaroni!

When Nick finished the tune, he took his hat from his head to look at it. His smile was as big and wide as the hat. He had a real sombrero.

"Everybody in Independence will know I've been to Santa Fe," he said proudly.

Story 2

The
Twins and Nell

AT THE END OF THE OREGON TRAIL

Jed Johnson was the first pioneer to go so far up the valley. He had built his cabin on the edge of the forest. Huge fir trees rose behind it. It seemed to his little sister Nell as though the sky rested on them.

Jed was working hard in the fields. Nell brought the twins out to see their father. They were a year and a half old. They were very young pioneers. They could just walk. Nell had a rope around her waist. Bob was tied to one end. Davy was tied to the other.

Trouble had come to the little cabin under the fir trees. Life in a pioneer cabin was hard. Mary, Jed's wife, lay ill.

236

"I've got to get Mary to a doctor," Jed said. "It's eight miles down the trail to the nearest town."

Ten-year-old Nell nodded. She looked very serious. She dug her bare toes into the soft earth.

"You'll have to stay alone with the twins," said Jed.

There were no neighbors yet to turn to for help. Jed had only one horse. He had lost his ox team on the way out. Jed had to drive a horse and a cow together for the plowing.

"I can hold Mary on the horse and walk beside her," said Jed. "But with only one horse I can't take the twins and you along."

"Don't you worry," said Nell. "I'll manage."

The cows were tied near the house where they could graze. Jed left the sheep and pigs in the barn. With bears and wolves around, the barn was almost like a fort. Jed barred the door.

Mary looked white and weak as Jed lifted her up on the horse. Jed would let her stop often and rest on a buffalo robe under a tree. Nell ran out with food for them to carry on the trip.

"There's a pistol on the shelf. It's loaded," said Jed softly. "A gun's too heavy for you."

Nell nodded. Pioneer women and girls, as well as men, must learn to handle guns. Jed had taught her to aim the big pistol and to fire.

237

Nell and the twins waved good-by. They watched the horse disappear down the trail. Then they turned back into the little room.

There was plenty for Nell to do. First, she tied the rope that held the twins to a peg. Then she ran out for more wood.

"Milk!" demanded Davy as she came back.

She filled a tin cup for him. He tipped it up. Nothing could be seen but his golden curls above it. Indian women loved to pat those curls. When they saw the twins, they smiled and reached out their hands.

Nell turned toward the fire. But the next second there came a loud wail from Bob. Davy was pouring his milk over Bob. Then he beat him on the head with the cup.

"Davy, stop it, you naughty boy!" cried Nell, as she snatched the cup away.

238

But Bob had stopped crying. He thought it was funny to have milk running off his nose.

"I'll take you two rascals out of doors," Nell said.

Two big spoons, some stones, and an iron kettle kept the twins busy for an hour. Nell sat with her knitting. Then Bob wanted Davy's spoon. They both began to cry. Nell ran in for some food. It was time for dinner.

Nell sat on the step with a big bowl of soup. A twin sat on either side of her. She fed first one and then the other. They opened their mouths like little birds.

After dinner, Nell tried to get the twins to take naps. They were very wide awake. They laughed and rolled over on the bed. Bob fell off one side of the bed. Davy fell off the other.

At last, Nell thought of something her grandmother had told her to do. Grandmother had said, "When you are at your wit's end with a baby, remember this. It will help you out."

Nell took a little molasses from the jug. She rubbed it on the babies' fat fingers. Then she pulled two little feathers from the feather bed. She gave each baby a feather. The feathers stuck to their fingers. The babies tried to pick them off with one hand but they only stuck to the other.

The twins stopped crying. This was a new game. They began to laugh and shout. But at last they grew sleepy. Eyes began to close. Nell did not mean to drop asleep too, but she was very tired. A fly buzzed. The smell of the fir trees came in the window. Soon all was quiet in the little house.

Nell slept soundly. Then, suddenly, she woke. She heard strange noises outside. For a moment she lay still. Then she jumped up. Oh, she should not have slept! What was happening? Something terrible?

The cows were mooing loudly. Then a rope broke and she heard the sound of running hoofs. Nell started toward the door. Then she stopped. She stood as still as though she had been turned to stone.

A huge black head was looking in at the door.

There came a low growl. It was a big black bear. Slowly he rose up on his hind legs and looked about. He seemed bigger than the whole house. He filled the whole doorway, but he did not come inside. Nell watched with horror.

Bears love sweets. This one had smelled the molasses. He reached out a huge paw. He reached for the molasses jug that Nell had left on the table close by the door. Nell could see sharp claws on the bear's paw. Those claws could tear off the hair from a man's head. One stroke from those great paws could crush a man.

Down tumbled the jug from the table. The molasses spilled and ran out the door and down the step. The bear dropped on all fours. Out came a long pink tongue. He began to lick up the delicious brown stream. Never had the big bear tasted anything so good.

Nell jumped forward. She snatched up the jug and threw it outside. It broke into a dozen pieces. She slammed the heavy door shut. She barred it safely. There was a surprised and angry growl from outside. A big paw scratched at the door. Then the bear found the rest of the molasses. He began to lick it up.

As Nell turned away from the door, she saw two small faces watching her from the bed. She saw four large blue eyes. Oh dear, she thought, now they'll be frightened and begin to cry.

But all Davy said was "Bow-wow!" in a sweet voice.

All that Bobby said was, "Bow-wow, all gone!"

Nell started to laugh and cry at the same time. She ran to the bed and hugged the twins.

What should she do next? She heard excited sounds from the barn. The animals smelled danger and were afraid. For a moment, Nell thought she heard the sound of a horse coming. Perhaps Jed was back! But Jed was many miles away.

"I have got to get rid of the beast!" thought Nell.

She looked at the pistol on the shelf. She was afraid of the big, heavy thing. She took it down carefully. Then she climbed onto a stool by the window. The bear was still outside, licking the broken jug. He was so near she could almost touch him.

243

Nell held the heavy pistol as steady as she could. She counted three and then fired. There came a loud, angry howl from outside. But Nell could not see what had happened. As the heavy pistol went off, her stool tipped over. Down she went, crash! When she got to her feet, there was no sign of the bear. But a trail of blood led off toward the woods.

It was late that night when Jed came home. The forest was as black as a pocket. He could not see the trail. But the tired horse knew the way.

Nell ran out to meet him. She tried to tell him everything at once. A bear had come. The cows had run off. She had wounded the bear, but not killed him. The twins were safe and asleep. How was Mary?

Jed threw his strong arms around Nell and held her close. He told her that Mary was comfortable. All she needed was rest and nursing. He was proud of Nell. She must not worry about the cows.

"I'll follow that bear's trail in the morning," said Jed. "We'll have a fine big bearskin to lay in front of the fire. It will be a warm place for the twins to play in winter."

Just then Nell heard a sound of trampling in the woods. She gripped Jed's arm. He raised his gun. Then he gave a laugh. A white face peered through the bushes. They could just see it in the starlight. It was one of the cows. Soon another joined her. They had come back to be milked.

Nell clapped her hands for joy. Then she ran for the milk pails.

Story 3

The Great News

AT THE END OF THE CALIFORNIA TRAIL

It was still dark. Fog blew in from the Pacific Ocean. Ken sat all alone on his small trunk. He was waiting for the stagecoach. He felt in his pocket for his money. Was it safe? Was it there? Yes, it was there.

His mother's name was on his trunk. It was put on in brass tacks. She seemed very far away. She was back in Iowa with the younger children. Ken felt very much alone.

There was one big question in Ken's mind. Would his father meet him? Would he find his father?

Ken had come west with neighbors. He had helped care for their cattle. For nearly two thousand miles he had walked. Day after day after day he had walked, following the long line of wagons. Now, at last, he was in San Francisco.

His friends had left him before the sun was up. They were going north. He was going south.

"You wait here till the stagecoach comes," they had said. "Good-by and good luck."

"Thanks and good-by," called Ken. He had felt very much alone as the wagons moved off into the fog.

Ken's father had come to California the year before. It seemed as though everybody in the world were rushing to California in the year 1849. Gold had been found in California.

Little gold had Ken's father found! He had nearly broken his back working up in the mountains. Then he had gone to the town of San Jose. He had started a store. He had done well. He had written for Ken to come out to help him. Ken was to come the first chance he had.

So here sat Ken in the fog, waiting for the stagecoach. Would his father meet him? Would he find his father? His mother had written that he had started, but it took months for letters to get to California in those days.

The fog began to lift. The sun rose round and red from behind the mountains. Ken walked up and down the road to get warm. Then, suddenly, he stopped.

He looked down on a lovely sight. The water was full of ships. People were coming to California by water as well as by land.

As Ken watched, another ship came sailing in. She was larger than the rest. She had great white sails. She was a clipper ship. In she came, through the opening that led in from the Pacific Ocean beyond. The Golden Gate, it is called now.

248

Ken gave a jump. Where was he? Was his trunk safe? Was it time for the stagecoach to start? He ran back to his place. A few people were already there. More were coming.

Now that the sun was up, the town awoke. People hurried here and there. Several coaches were to start off in different directions.

Men hurried through the crowd. "This way, sir," they shouted. "Here you are, ma'am. Your stage will start from over there."

"Where will my stage be? Where should I wait?" cried a woman. She had three children and a big pile of boxes and a trunk.

"This way, ma'am," shouted one man. "Have your trunk weighed."

"What? Fifteen dollars to take that trunk?" cried the woman.

"Leave it in the middle of the road, if you'd rather," said the man.

There was nothing to do but pay. Just then the first stagecoach drove in. The woman hurried her children aboard.

Ken watched anxiously for the coach for San Jose. Soon it came. It was a fine sight, with six black horses. They were eager to be off. Men held the heads of the lead horses.

"Up you go if you have the fare, son," shouted a big man with a red face.

Ken counted out his money. He had just enough for himself and his trunk. He climbed to a seat on top of the coach. A woman with a wide skirt and a big hat box sat next him. Her skirt nearly covered him up.

"Just think!" she said to Ken. "We're going sixty miles in six hours. I hope we don't have an accident. My sister was in a stagecoach that went rolling over a cliff — people, horses, and all together. It was dreadful."

"No accidents on this line," called the driver. "This line has Concord coaches. None better made. This coach, here, came all the way from Concord, New Hampshire, way back East."

250

"How did it get over the mountains?" asked Ken.

"Came round South America by boat," said the driver.

There was no more talk. Just then came shouting and cheering. Something exciting had happened. Ken jumped up in his place to see. Men were throwing their hats into the air. Guns were being fired.

Great news had just reached San Francisco. California had been made a state!

Another star had been added to the flag of the United States of America. It was a star for the new state of California. It was the thirty-first star, for the United States had been growing since Washington's day. Now there were thirty-one states instead of thirteen.

"California has been made a state!" everyone shouted.

Ken nearly fell off his seat, but the woman next to him kept a hold on his coat.

Then a man in a wide hat came pushing through the crowd. He was the Governor. He was to carry the news to the people in San Jose. Onto the coach where Ken sat, climbed the Governor.

A horn blew. The men jumped back from the horses' heads. Off the horses galloped.

Ken held his breath. It seemed like flying. He had never ridden so fast before. The coach was hung on heavy leather straps. It rocked to and fro.

Then Ken saw, through the dust, that there was another coach beside them. There were two stagecoaches going to San Jose. Which would get there first? Which would carry the news?

Off across the bare, flat ground the horses galloped. The drivers did not trouble to keep on a road. Off toward the brown hills the two coaches raced.

People along the way ran out to see why the stagecoaches were going so fast.

"California is a state!" everyone shouted.

The horses' sides were covered with foam. They were panting. They were tired. But a race is a race. Neither coach would let the other coach get ahead.

252

At last a low brick building came in sight. Fresh horses waited there. The horses made a last plunge. Up to the building rattled the coach on which Ken rode. It was now well ahead.

It did not take many minutes to change horses. Fresh ones were ready. Away they galloped. Ken's coach was still in the lead.

The way grew rougher. Suddenly there came a terrible bump. Ken flew into the air. He came down on the hat box of the lady next to him. People screamed. The coach stopped. A wheel was caught in a hole. The horses strained and pulled. They could not get it out.

Men jumped down to help the horses. But while they worked, the other coach went thundering past. It was a dreadful moment. Ken wanted to howl with rage.

Just then the men and horses got the wheel free. In another moment they were tearing along. Little by little, they gained on the other coach.

"We've got to win!" shouted Ken. "We've got to win! The Governor's aboard!"

"We're going to win!" said the driver. He knew his horses. He urged them on.

Never was there such a ride. The horses galloped neck to neck. The people were nearly shaken to

254

pieces. Ken shouted so much that he could hardly speak.

It was two o'clock when the stages dashed into San Jose. The coach on which Ken rode was just ahead. It had won the race. The horses were pulled to a halt. The coaches stopped.

"California is a state!" shouted the driver.

People came running from every side. They cheered and clapped. People began climbing down from the stagecoach. Suddenly Ken felt very much alone.

He could see no one he knew. In all the excitement, he had forgotten that he was all alone. Would his father meet him? Would he find his father? What should he do if no one met him? Perhaps his mother's letter had not arrived.

For a few moments Ken stood by his small trunk and looked around.

"Waiting for someone?" asked a man.

"I'm looking for my father," said Ken.

"California is a pretty big place to lose your father in," said the man.

Just then Ken saw a tall man coming toward him. He had a wide hat and a long black beard. He wore a pistol at his belt. Ken looked at him carefully. Then he gave a cry of surprise.

255

The tall man was coming straight toward him. It was his father. Ken had not known him with a beard. It was nearly two years since he had seen his father.

The next minute Ken was given a big hug and swung off his feet. In all the excitement he did not forget to tell the news.

"California is a state!" cried Ken. "And we brought the Governor, and our stagecoach won the race, and here I am!"

"Ready to grow up with the country," laughed his father. "I'm glad you're here at last. I've been meeting stagecoaches ever since your mother's letter came."

Ken's father picked up the trunk and carried it on his shoulder.

"It's good to see your mother's old trunk," he said. "I hope she and the other children will be coming out next year."

Ken followed his father through the little town. It had been a Spanish town once. Now it was filled with pioneers from many lands. The bells still hung in the old church that Spanish priests had built for the Indians. The bells rang out to welcome Ken to his new home.

HOW THE BLACKSMITH WORKED

1.

2.

Big bellows blew the fire and made it blaze. The place where the fire burned was called the forge. The blacksmith wore a heavy leather apron.

The blacksmith held a piece of iron in the fire. He held it in a pair of tongs. The iron became red hot. Then it was so hot that it turned white.

3.

4.

The iron became soft because it was so very hot. Then the blacksmith hammered it on his anvil. Sparks flew from the hot iron.

The blacksmith made many things that the pioneers used. He made plows, shovels, and axes. He mended wagon wheels and chains.

5.

In his spare time the blacksmith made nails. Each nail had to be made by hand. He made hinges for doors, and latches to hold them shut.

6.

He made iron kettles and pots. He made the cranes and the pothooks to hold the kettles over the fire. He made iron spoons and knives and forks.

7.

When a horse needed a new shoe the blacksmith pounded the iron into a horseshoe. Then he cooled it in a tub of water.

8.

He cut away some of the horse's hoof and fitted the shoe. Then he nailed it on with nails he had made himself.

Things to Talk About

1. Can you read these names?

Independence	Missouri	Santa Fe
Columbia River	California	San Francisco
Rocky Mountains	Oregon	Pacific Ocean

   There is both a state and a river named Missouri. Find the places on a map.

2. These are other names that you have had. Which are names of rivers? Which are names of towns? Which are names of people?

Mississippi	St. Augustine	George Washington
Plymouth	Boone	New Amsterdam
Philadelphia	Columbus	Ohio
Pocahontas	New York	Detroit

3. What are these the names of? Atlantic   Pacific

4. These stories tell about three trails west. What were the three trails called?

5. Make up riddles about some of the names on this page. Choose someone to guess the answer. Here is one.

   Which city was started by the French people? The white people and the Indians met there to trade. Thousands of automobiles are made there now.

6. Why did Nick think mules were best in the desert?

7. How were stagecoaches different from buses?

8. Find on the map how the Concord coaches got out to California.

260

Things to Do

1. Look at the picture on page 236. Then close your book. Write the numbers from one to ten on a piece of paper. Ask someone to read the list below. Read the number first. If the words tell about the picture write YES after the number. If not, write NO.

   1. log cabin
   2. the twins
   3. man at the door
   4. dark trees
   5. a river

   6. a covered wagon
   7. two skins on the wall
   8. two windows
   9. a cow
   10. a chimney

   Now look at the picture again. Read over the list to see how many you have correct. Play the same game with another picture tomorrow.

2. In the picture on page 236, what is the round thing near the barrel? Why do you think it was useful to a pioneer?

3. Which of these three stories do you think would make the best play? Act it out.

Things to Find Out

1. Visit a blacksmith shop if there is one near you. If not, ask your father or some man you know if he saw a blacksmith shop when he was a boy. Make a list of things that you would find in a blacksmith shop.

2. What things do you know that are made of iron or steel?

3. Look on page 240. What do you think it means to be "at your wit's end"?

11 Home on the Plains

A STORY OF PIONEERS
FROM NORWAY

Home
on the Plains

Pioneers had rushed to California to try to find gold. Many stayed and built homes along the Pacific Ocean. There were many cities and towns and farms all the way from the Atlantic Ocean to beyond the Mississippi River. Yet in the middle part of our country, Indians still lived on the Great Plains.

Then, little by little, the last pioneers began moving onto the Great Plains. Little by little, they took the last of the Indians' land.

Indian chiefs called their young warriors together. They tried to keep their land. A thousand battles were fought. Many pioneers and many Indians were killed.

Some of the Indians were paid a little for their land, but money did not make up for lost homes and lost hunting grounds. A little land was still left to them, but it was poor land.

264

As the years went by, more and more people came to this country to live. In 1862 a law was passed that gave free farmland to anyone who would go west and live on it. More and more pioneers hurried west.

Some of these pioneers came from the country of Norway. Norway is a country by the sea. In Norway, steep cliffs drop down to the water. Deep forests cover much of the land.

The Great Plains were very different from the land that these pioneers had left. Often there was not one tree in sight on the Great Plains. Mile after mile of grassy land stretched away. The winds howled in winter. The hot sun beat down in summer. Pioneers from Norway found this new land very strange.

There were so few trees that it was hard to build houses. These pioneers had to build their first houses out of sod. They cut squares of sod, and piled them on top of each other.

Little by little, sod houses took the place of Indian tepees. Children from Norway now played where Indians had once sat by campfires and watched the war dance. Men plowed the ground where buffaloes had grazed.

What was it like, coming from Norway to build a sod home on this great, lonely plain? The next story will tell you.

The Sod House

Chapter 1. BREAKING EARTH

A sod house! That was a strange thing. A lump came in Hilda's throat. She did not want to live in a sod house.

The two older boys, Olaf and Eric, did not care what kind of house they lived in. It was this fine rich land that pleased them. It was wonderful land to plow and to plant. It was as flat as your hand. It had cost them nothing.

"Come on, boys," shouted Father. "Fasten the oxen to the plow. We'll break the earth."

Hilda looked about. She looked out over the big, lonely, empty land. She had never thought that there could be such a land.

The boys lifted a plow from one of the wagons that had brought them to this place. They fastened two of the oxen to the plow.

"Here we go!" shouted Father.

Father held the plow firmly. He pressed it into the earth. The boys led the oxen. Off they started. Slowly the plow cut a deep, long black line into the earth. The boys cheered. It was an exciting moment.

"It's fine rich earth," said Mother.

Back and forth went the plow, turning up the sod. While the oxen rested, the boys cut the sod into squares. They left the squares to dry in the sun. They would use them to make a house.

But Hilda did not want to live in a sod house. She thought of Grandmother's neat house back in Norway. There were gay curtains at the windows and big feather beds to sleep in. On summer days, salt breezes from the ocean blew in. How Hilda wished that she could run down to the shore now to watch the fishing boats!

"We can let the sod house wait till cold weather," said Father. "We can live in the tent for a while." He wanted to get the fields plowed.

Mother was firm. "We must have a house. The fields can wait," she said.

So the house was started at once. Each day the sod walls grew higher.

"You can't use sod for a roof," said Hilda. "What will we have for a roof?"

"This house isn't going to have any roof," teased Olaf.

"Snow will keep you warm in winter," teased Eric.

"Go, get your work done," said Mother. "Of course there's going to be a roof, Hilda. Father will have to get logs to hold it."

268

Father hated to stop to go for the logs. But the boys thought that a trip would be fun. Some trees grew near a river, several miles away. The boys could swim, after the logs were cut.

The next day, Father and the boys started off. Hilda helped her mother wash clothes at the spring near by. There was bread to bake in an open iron oven by the campfire. Then Hilda and her mother sat down to patch the boys' shirts.

The day grew very hot. It was like an oven inside the tent. Suddenly Hilda could stand it no longer.

"I hate it here!" she sobbed. "I want to go back home."

Mother stroked Hilda's hair. "There, dear," she said softly. "You're homesick. It's best to cry it out."

"Why did we have to come?" cried Hilda.

"It's this fine land your father wants," said her mother. "It was a hard life in Norway for your father, fishing in the winter storms."

"Can't we go back?" asked Hilda.

"It would break your father's heart," said her mother. "Come, shut your eyes and take a nap. I'll tell you a story about when I was a little girl."

She told about the day in Norway when the cows were driven way up on the mountains to graze. She had gone along and had lost her way. The women had called and the men had hunted. There was a great to-do! Then at last she had been found. She was curled up beside a big cow who was lying down chewing her cud. There she was, lying fast asleep.

On went Mother's voice until Hilda, too, was asleep. Mother sat looking at her. It was a hard country for a little girl. The boys were all right. One minute they were chasing prairie dogs. The next minute they were begging their father to let them shoot ducks with the gun. They were up to plenty of mischief, those boys. It was harder for a girl.

Chapter 2. WINTER

Snow came early that year. The sod hut was done in time. There was only one room and a shed for the oxen, but it was done.

The air was so full of snowflakes that Hilda could not see out of either little window. Much good it did to have windows! The house was dark and dreary.

It was lucky that Father and the boys had spent two weeks cutting wood for the fire. The little iron stove was kept red hot. But the sod walls of the house and the dirt floor were damp and cold.

271

Father and Eric had made a trip to the nearest town. They had bought flour, bacon, beans, and coffee and sugar. There was enough to eat in the little sod house, but there was little fun. The one room was too crowded. Olaf and Eric began to quarrel. Then Eric teased Hilda.

"School!" said Mother firmly. "What you three need is school."

She took out a Bible and a spelling book from the big chest that had come with them. Father split slabs of wood to write on. Charcoal could be used for pencils.

Hilda wanted to draw pictures of the sea and rocks and boats. But Mother said, "No drawing, till lessons are learned."

In the evenings they sang. Mother had a sweet voice. The children learned all the old songs.

It was only December. There were January, February, and March still ahead. It seemed to Hilda as though the snow would never stop. Oh, how she longed for other girls to play with!

Some of the days were fair. The sun shone so brightly then that the light on the snow was blinding. The boys made skis. Olaf fell into a snowbank. His two skis waved in the air. Eric and his father had to come and pull him out.

272

At last January and February passed. As March came, Mother began to watch the food with care. The flour was low. The bacon was almost gone.

"How soon can you make a trip to town?" asked Mother.

The sugar and coffee gave out, but still Father said, "Not quite yet."

Then one sunny morning he said, "The snow's nearly gone. We'll start today. We'll be back the day after tomorrow."

Eric had gone to town in the fall. It was Olaf's turn now.

"Will Mother and I never go to town?" thought Hilda. "It's always the boys and Father who go."

Hilda watched the wagon move off across the wide plain. The land was so flat that she could see the wagon for nearly an hour. It grew smaller and smaller. Then it disappeared. Tears came to Hilda's eyes.

For two days the warm spring breeze blew. Then, on the third day, the wind changed. Clouds raced across the sky. The air filled with snow.

There was no sleep in the sod house that night. Eric kept the stove red hot. Mother kept food warm. Everyone was thinking of the biting wind and the snow. No one could forget the ox team struggling through the storm.

There came a sound at the door. Mother jumped to her feet, but it was only the wind.

274

Eric could sit still no longer. "Let me take my skis and go out to meet them," he begged.

"You have no way of finding them in the storm," said his mother.

A noise came again. Eric ran to the door. Then the others followed him. This time it must be something besides the wind. Suddenly the door swung open. In came the icy wind. In came, also, a tall white snowman. He had something in his arms. It was Father carrying Olaf.

"Get the oxen under cover as fast as you can, Eric," shouted Father. "See that they get extra food."

Olaf lay on the bed. Mother and Hilda rubbed his face and feet with snow to bring the blood back into them. Father walked back and forth swinging his arms and stamping. He drank a big bowl of hot soup.

At last Olaf opened his eyes. He was warm, and he was sleepy, so sleepy. When Father saw that Olaf was all right, he threw himself down beside the boy. The two slept as though they would never wake again.

The next morning Father and Olaf told of the trip. They had reached the town safely. They had bought all they needed and started for home. They were only ten miles from home when the snow came. They could not tell which way to go. No tracks showed.

275

They had wandered about in the snow and wind for eight hours. But at last the oxen had found the way. The patient beasts had finally found their way home.

Hilda sat and listened. This was a terrible land of cold and storms. In summer it was hot. The sun was a ball of fire. In winter the storms blew across the plains. The snow piled up until the houses were nearly covered with it. People were buried in snow and froze to death within a mile of their own homes. It was a cruel land.

"I have plenty of seed for the fields," said Father. "We'll sow wheat as soon as the snow melts."

"He is thinking only of his fields," thought Hilda bitterly. "He has already forgotten the terrible trip."

She gave a sigh. She hated this strange new land.

Chapter 3. SPRING

Spring flowers came at last. Little frogs sang, down by the spring. Father and the boys worked early and late.

Then one day Eric came racing toward the house. "Someone is coming!" he shouted.

Was it Indians? The Indians had been angry and bitter of late. They hated to have the white men taking their land.

Father got his gun. All of the family quickly climbed to the roof of the sod house. Then, far off across the prairie, they saw a line of wagons.

277

"Covered wagons," shouted Olaf.

"It's a whole village," cried Eric.

There were six wagons, a dozen cows, and some horses. Father and the boys ran out to meet them. Hilda followed more slowly. She wondered who these newcomers were.

Mother put the coffee pot on the stove. The travelers must stop. They must come in and eat fresh bread and drink hot coffee.

It was months since Mother had seen other women. She got out the best she had. Father took the men out at once to look at his fields. No more work that day!

Eric and Olaf found boys their own age. At first, Hilda stood alone watching. There were no other girls. Then suddenly her face brightened. There were babies being lifted out of the wagons. Three babies and a little one who could just walk. She ran over to them.

"Here, Hilda," said her mother. "Hold this one."

Hilda took a fat roly-poly baby in her arms. The baby began to laugh and crow. Hilda held her tightly.

For the next two days Hilda forgot how lonely she had been. She played with the babies all day. One of them slept with her at night. The one who could just walk followed her everywhere she went.

278

For two days the wagon train camped near the sod house. One man had a fiddle. He played for dancing each evening.

"Oh," thought Hilda, "perhaps these people will take up land here near us. Now perhaps we shall have neighbors."

Father showed the men what good land it was. He urged them to stay. There was much talk, but it did no good. The people decided to go farther.

So they were not to have neighbors after all! The boys were very sad. It did not seem to Hilda as though she could say good-by to the babies.

But there was nothing to be done about it. Off moved the long line of wagons. But one wagon stayed behind.

Hilda's mother called to her. "I want to talk to you, Hilda," said Mother quietly. "One of these families has decided to turn back. They are going back to Norway. You could go with them."

"Oh, Mother," began Hilda. Her heart beat fast.

"You could go back to live with Grandmother," said Mother.

Hilda looked at her mother. She could hardly believe her ears. Go back to Norway! Have other girls to play with! Have a real house to live in!

Then suddenly Hilda stopped. Could she leave her mother? Next winter could she be happy in the big warm kitchen at Grandmother's? Could she forget the little sod house on the plains? When she grew up and told stories to her own little girls, how would she feel? The boys would tell their sons of the first years of "breaking earth." She would have to say that she had given up and gone back to Grandmother's.

Hilda threw her arms about her mother. "I'll stay here! I'll never go back!" she cried. "I don't care what happens!"

"Think well, Hilda," said her mother. "Winter will come again. It is a long, hard time."

"I have thought," cried Hilda. "I'm going to stay here with you and Father and the boys."

Just then there came a cheer. Hilda jumped with surprise. Her father was standing just behind her. He caught her up in his arms and hugged her.

"Good for you, Hilda!" he said. "You are going to stand by us! In a few years we'll have a better house. You'll see!"

Two heads looked in at the door. Two pairs of blue eyes looked at Hilda. So Olaf and Eric knew, too!

280

Eric and Olaf wanted to know what she had decided. They wanted her to stay!

"Hilda is not going away!" said their father. "She's going to stay with us."

There were shouts from the two boys. They turned cart wheels and stood on their heads. Hilda laughed in spite of herself. Suddenly she was happy.

"I'll teach you how to ski this winter," said Eric.

"I'll make you a sled," said Olaf.

"And I have news," said Father. "A man has just ridden by. The other wagons have turned around. They are coming back to take up land here. We shall have neighbors after all."

Hilda jumped up and clapped her hands. The babies were coming back. She was staying with Mother and Father and the boys. Living in a sod house was not going to be so bad after all.

HOW THE PIONEERS RAISED CORN AND WHEAT

1.

2.

Corn was planted in little hills. Four kernels were put in each. The Indians had corn before the pioneers came. They taught the pioneers how to plant it.

Corn was easy to use. As soon as the ears were ripe, they could be roasted and eaten. Or else the corn could be dried and saved to use later.

3.

4.

Corn was often pounded into yellow corn meal in a hollow log. Sometimes a small tree was fastened to the pounder to help lift it up and down.

In the fall the cornstalks were tied into stacks. They looked like Indian tepees. The children played in them and made corn cob dolls.

5.

Corn would grow in rough ground. Wheat needed well-cleared ground. Stones had to be taken away so that the plow could cut into the earth.

6.

Ripe wheat could not be eaten at once. The seeds must be beaten from the stalks. Then the wheat was tossed in the air and the straw was blown away.

7.

Corn and wheat were ground between two big mill stones. Water from a stream turned the stones round and round.

8.

Corn meal made good bread. Corn meal kept better than wheat flour. But wheat flour made cakes and good bread, too.

Things to Talk About

1. What are the names of the children in the story *Home on the Plains?*

2. Why was the new home better for the boys than for Hilda?

3. What were some of the things about her old home that Hilda longed for in her new home?

4. What was the name of the country from which Hilda had come?

5. What did Hilda's mother find for the children to do in winter?

6. Do you think that Hilda was glad when she grew up that she had stayed in the sod hut?

7. How did Olaf and Eric feel about Hilda's staying with them?

8. What was the good news that Father brought?

9. Look on page 265. Tell what the Great Plains were like in summer and in winter. Tell how they have changed. Shut your eyes and see if you can see these word pictures.

   "Children from Norway now played where Indians had once sat by campfires and watched the war dance."

   "Men plowed the ground where buffaloes had once grazed."

10. Draw pictures of these scenes.

Things to Do

1. Look back at the stories in the book. Pick out a scene from one of them to act. Choose someone to guess the scene you are acting.

2. Draw a picture of a scene. Hold it up for the class to guess what it shows.

3. Which story did you like best in the book? Tell why you liked it best.

4. Ask your teacher to write on the blackboard all the names that you can think of that you have read about in this book. Make headings like these:

   Places   Oceans   Rivers   People

5. See if you can find five of the places on a map.

Things to Find Out

1. Look on page 276. Find words that tell about oxen.

2. Look on page 278. Find a word that tells about a baby.

3. Look on page 281. Find the words that tell three things that the boys did when they heard that Hilda was to stay with them.

4. Look on page 282. How was corn planted? Can you eat corn as soon as it is ripe? Tell some of the differences between corn and wheat. Which was better for the pioneers?

12

The
Greatest Pioneer of All

The
Greatest Pioneer
of All

The greatest pioneer of them all was born in a
one-room cabin. His father had built it of logs. It had
no window. The floor was dirt. The mother and baby
lay on a rough bed with a bear skin thrown over them.

The baby was dressed in a little yellow skirt and a
tiny linen shirt. They were of homespun. He was
small and red.

A neighbor's boy came from down the road to look
at the new baby.

"He won't amount to much," said the boy.

The little pioneer grew bigger. He had few chances
to go to school. He learned to read. He read every
book that he could get hold of. He read by the light
of the open fire. He learned to write with a bit of
charcoal.

When he was eight years old he could swing an ax. He learned to cut down trees and to split logs into fence rails. His father kept moving west. The baby had been born in Kentucky. Then the family moved to Indiana. Then they moved to Illinois. Each time they moved, the boy helped his father build a new log cabin.

He grew very tall. He grew very strong. His first long trip away from home was by flatboat down the Mississippi River. People said that you could always trust him. People said that he was fair and wise and honest.

At last, more and more people came to know this boy who had grown to be a man. More and more people liked to hear him talk. He told funny stories. He made people laugh. He also made people think. He could be serious as well as funny.

At last came a day when the people of the United States were voting for a new President. There was great excitement in the land. Who was to be the next President? Who would be chosen?

A tall man waited for the news. He was homely and he was awkward, but he had kind eyes. If anyone did a mean or cruel thing, his face was stern. If anyone needed help, his face was kind. His smile made people feel at home.

The tall man waited for news. Who was to be the next President?

At last word came. The tall man had been chosen. He was to go to Washington to live in the White House. His name was Abraham Lincoln.

So this pioneer baby, born in a log cabin, grew up and went to the White House. This little boy grew up to become the President of the United States of America.

There had been great changes in our country by the time Abraham Lincoln became President. Men had invented many new things. Slowly our land was changing from a land of log cabins and homespun cloth. Machines and engines were being invented.

A machine was invented to spin thread. One person at a machine could spin in a day as much as a thousand women with spinning wheels.

An engine was invented to run a boat.

"A boat run by an engine!" some people cried. "It will blow up. It is not safe." And some of the first engines did blow up.

Engines were invented to pull trains. Tracks were laid for them to run on. At first, cows walked along the tracks and got in the way. Sparks from the engines set fire to ladies' hats as they rode on the coaches.

When young Abe Lincoln moved to Illinois with his father, he went in a big, homemade wagon. But when Abraham Lincoln went to Washington in 1861, he did not go by covered wagon. He did not even go on horseback or in a stagecoach. He went on a train.

It was very different from our trains today. The engine had a tall smokestack. Black smoke streamed from it. But it could go more than twenty miles an hour. It could go farther in one hour than a covered wagon could go in a day.

More and more miles of railroad track were being laid each year. By 1861 trains ran as far west as the Missouri River. There was even talk of building a track all the way across our country to California. But many people said that was all nonsense. From the Missouri River to California was eighteen hundred long miles.

"Build a track across the plains?" the people cried. "Indians would attack! Buffaloes would block the way. What about the deserts and high mountains? You can't teach the engine to run up and down mountains!"

Lincoln listened to both sides. But he had watched the long lines of covered wagons. He had seen hundreds of men, women, and children starting west from the Missouri River. *Eighteen hundred miles!* That

291

trip would take them four or five long, hard months. Some would never get to California. There should be an easier way.

Again Lincoln wondered, How can our country be strong and united if it takes so long to cross it? How can we Americans understand one another and work together if we cannot travel easily across our great land?

After Lincoln was made President, he signed a paper. It said that a new railroad was to be started. The *transcontinental railroad*, it was called. *Trans* means *across*. *Transcontinental* means across the continent. Two companies were to build the road. One company was to start building west from the Missouri River. The other company was to start building east from California. Men in New York and in San Francisco were to direct the work. When the two tracks met, the railway would be done.

There were no bulldozers in those days. There were no caterpillar tractors with derricks or cranes. Men must dig with pick and shovel. They must carry dirt in wheelbarrows. They must lift rails onto and off of wagons. The transcontinental railway must be built by hand.

Thousands of men and hundreds of teams of horses and mules and oxen started work. Most of the men

292

who started work at the Missouri had come to this country from Ireland. Most of the men who started work in California came from a very different part of the world from Ireland. They spoke no English. They wore loose blue suits and straw hats tied on their heads. They had pigtails down their backs. They came from the great land of China.

But, Irish or Chinese, the workmen were doing something that had never been done before. They were to build a railway such as the world had never seen. They, too, were pioneers.

What was it like working on the transcontinental railroad? What was it like when, after five years of work, the last rails were laid? The next story will tell you.

The Transcontinental Railroad

Chapter 1. BUILDING THE RAILROAD

Mike and his father had come from Ireland. Ireland, with its green fields, was a long way off. Ireland was very different from this strange land.

Sometimes Mike was homesick. But his father's farm had been poor. The potato crop had failed. There had been little or nothing to eat. Then his mother had died. Mike's father had sold the farm, and little did he get for it. There was just enough money to bring the two of them to America. Now they were working on the railroad.

Mike's father was boss of his rail gang. He was a fast worker. Mike was proud of him. Mike, himself, was a water boy. He carried pails of water to the thirsty men.

Mike's hair was red. When he was excited, it stood

straight up. His eyes were as blue as the lakes in Ireland. But now he was frowning and they looked dark as thunderclouds. His back ached and his hands were sore.

"I've carried enough water to float a ship!" muttered Mike.

He set his two pails down a minute to rest.

A loud, angry shout came. "Hi there, boy! Water!"

Mike grabbed his pails. A little water spilled. Mike gasped. Waste water! Water was precious in this desert land where the men were working now. Mike

295

hurried on carefully with his pails. A man grabbed a long-handled dipper. He drank and drank. The water was stale from standing in barrels. It was warm from the sun, but at least it was wet.

Each day trains brought up supplies. As soon as tracks were laid, the engines began running over them. Each day the engines could go a little farther before they came to "end of track," as the men called it. Sometimes a mile of track was laid in a day. Sometimes two miles. Sometimes even more.

The trains brought up railway ties and iron rails, spikes, and bolts. They brought up all the food for the men and hay for the horses and mules. Now "end of track" was in the desert and they had to bring water as well. The water boys carried it in pails from the siding where the flatcars stood.

Back and forth went Mike. The air was full of dust from the heavy wagons. The dust turned gold in the sun, but it made Mike choke and cough. The air was full of noise as well. Wagons pounded past. Men shouted. Clang, clang came the sound of the hammers as the men drove in the spikes.

Suddenly there came another sound. It was right behind Mike. Thud, thud came the sound of hoofs. There was a shout. Mike jumped aside. He fell rolling in the dust. A big black horse went galloping by.

A boy rode on the horse's back. He was shouting at people to get out of the way. He was urging the horse on. The horse galloped down the track. Behind the horse was a long rope fastened to a rail-truck, bringing up more rails for the men at "end of track."

Mike watched the horse. Sparks flew as his iron shoe hit a stone. Oh, how Mike longed to ride such a horse! How he longed to go galloping down the track shouting! But there was no horse for Mike. He plodded on down the path in the dust and noise with his empty pails.

Now the day's work was nearly over. No more water was needed. Mike ran over to watch his father's gang before they stopped work.

There were a few more rails to lay. The men worked fast. There were five in each gang. The men rolled a rail from the rail-truck. Three men grabbed it on one end and two men grabbed it on the other end. Quickly they slung it into its place on the wooden ties. Men with big hammers stood ready and waiting.

Then Mike's father shouted, "DOWN." Clang, clang went the hammers driving in the spikes. Ten spikes to each rail. Three blows to each spike. It took just half a minute to lay a rail. Two rails a minute. The "end of track" moved forward.

Chapter 2. FASTER! FASTER!

Nearer and nearer together came the two lines of track. Now a race started between the Irish and the Chinese workers to see how much track could be laid in a day.

"Faster, faster!" went the cry.

The race was on. The men were eager and excited. The Irish worked hard to beat the Chinese. The Chinese worked equally hard to beat the Irish.

At night, the Irish told stories about those Chinese workers. Mike listened in wonder. His red hair stood on end. The Irish had done their share of hard work. They had laid the track over mountains and across the desert under the burning August sun. They had fought Indians. But the Chinese had had their share of hardship.

In the mountains, there were places where cliffs dropped straight down two thousand feet. There was no place for the tracks. A shelf must be cut in the side of the steep rock wall. The Chinese workers were let down by ropes. There they hung above the precipice. They chipped the rock away by hand. If the ropes broke! Mike's eyes grew large as he thought of what would happen.

298

But that was not all. The Chinese had cut tunnels through the mountains. They had blasted away the rock. But there was no dynamite in those days. Gunpowder was used to break up the rock. It was far more dangerous than dynamite. The men must light the gunpowder and then run. Sometimes they could not run fast enough.

One year, a thousand Chinese had worked in a tunnel all through the cold dark winter. It had taken two thousand men just to shovel away the snow and keep supplies coming to them. The Chinese ate their rice and they drank their tea and they dug away deep in the ground.

Mike wondered about these Chinese. They were strangers. They were different. He was not sure that he liked them. He wondered what they were like. Once he had seen some of them driving a supply wagon. There was a boy about his own age. The Irish boys had laughed at him. They had pointed at his straw hat, his loose blue cotton clothes, and his pigtail. But the Chinese boy had paid no attention to them.

At last news came that made every Irishman sit up. Each day the workers on both sides had been trying to lay a little more track than the day before. Each day they tried to work faster. Now came news. The Chinese had laid *six miles* of track in one day! Never had there been such a record.

Mike heard the men around him mutter, "We'll show them!"

Never had the work gone so quickly as it did the next day! Rail-trucks thundered along. Hammers clanged. Mike raced back and forth with his water buckets. He did not feel hot and tired. During the day word came in. "Four miles finished. Five miles. Six miles!" Everyone cheered. They would break the record the Chinese workers had set!

Then something unexpected happened to Mike. He was hurrying along the path. A rail-truck came pounding down the track. The big black horse was galloping. He was tired. He was covered with foam, but the boy on his back urged him on.

Suddenly the big animal stumbled. The boy went flying over his head. He lay on the ground. The horse stood still. Luckily at that spot the track ran up a little hill, so the heavy truck came slowly to a stop.

300

Mike ran to the boy. He knelt beside him. Was he badly hurt?

All at once the boy opened his eyes. He sat up. Then he began to shout at Mike. "Get on with that load of rails!" he screamed. "Get those rails to end of track! Don't stop here."

For half a second Mike looked at him. Then Mike grinned. His eyes flashed blue. He ran to the horse and started to climb up onto his back. It was a long way up but Mike made it.

"Gettee-up!" shouted Mike. The horse broke into a gallop. Mike bounced up and down. At first he thought he would be bounced to bits, but he held on for dear life. Down the track galloped the horse with the truck behind.

The men who were waiting were angry. They did not look to see who was on the horse.

"Where have you been, boy?" shouted a red-faced man. He threw a log under the truck to stop it.

Mike had no time to explain. He pulled up his horse so fast that he went flying up onto the horse's neck. He had to grab the animal's ears to keep from going over his head. Quickly he wiggled back into place.

Then Mike's father saw who was riding the horse.

"Good work, son! Keep the rails a-coming!" his father shouted.

When the truck was empty, the men tipped it off the track. Up galloped the next horse with more rails. While Mike waited, he patted his horse's neck. He talked gently to him. The horse whinnied.

"He's tired," thought Mike, "but he likes me."

Then Mike's truck was lifted back onto the track. Down the path he went. He bounced about less now. He was getting used to the horse. Back and forth along the track he rode, proudly.

That night there was good news. *Seven and a half miles* of track had been laid. There were cheers and celebrations, but they did not last long.

Soon word came back from the other side. "Tomorrow we will finish *ten miles* in one day!" Ten miles! That was impossible!

The railway was nearly finished by now. The tracks were coming very close together. Indeed they were so close that it was decided to give the Irish workers a holiday to go to see the fun. Ten miles of track in a day! Impossible!

Mike was up before daybreak. He rode with his father and a crowd of men in a big wagon. Across the desert they rode. Then Mike saw the other track shining in the sunrise. It had come all the way from California to meet them.

Five long trains stood ready with rails and spikes. At seven o'clock the signal to start work was given. Mike watched the Chinese workers hurry to their places. They were shorter than the Irish. They were slender and wiry. Then Mike's eyes opened wide. Never had he seen men work so fast! Fifteen seconds and a rail was down.

By noon six miles were down. By seven o'clock that evening ten miles were done! An engine ran triumphantly over the track.

The Irish went grumbling back to their own camp. The record was broken. Ten miles! And what was worse, there was nothing that they could do about it. The railroad was too nearly finished. They had only *six more miles* of track left to lay.

"We *could* have beaten them!" said Mike firmly. It was not fair. He almost hated those Chinese. "We could have done eleven miles if we'd had the chance!"

Chapter 3. END OF TRACK

There was a great celebration when the last rails were laid. Famous people came from all over the country to watch. Everyone was excited and happy. The place where the two tracks met was in the state of Utah, at a place called Promontory Point. It was near the Great Salt Lake.

Trains came up on the tracks from both directions. They brought crowds of men in high silk hats. They brought ladies in long silk dresses and children in fine clothes. Never in his life had Mike seen such a wonderful sight.

There were people from every part of our country. There were strong young men from Salt Lake City. They had helped with the grading of the land for the railway. There were Negroes and Mexicans, for some of them, too, had been working. Irish and Chinese swarmed everywhere. A few tall, silent Indians sat on their horses and watched.

At last everything was ready. Two engines stood facing each other. Then the last pair of rails was laid between them. A band played. There were speeches. Then a gentleman lifted a big hammer. He drove in the last spike in the transcontinental railroad. That spike was made of pure gold.

The two engines steamed forward until they touched. The people clapped and shouted and threw their caps into the air. The whistles on the engines blew until Mike thought his ears would burst. Bells began to ring. Men fired their guns into the air. The horses were frightened. Mules brayed. Then the band began to play so loud that you could not hear your own voice.

Mike was screaming as loud as anyone. He was jumping up and down. Suddenly he saw that he was standing beside the Chinese boy. Mike forgot that he did not like these Chinese. Before he knew it the two boys were clapping each other on the back. They were laughing and shouting and shaking hands. Then they turned cart wheels and tumbled over on the ground.

Mike's hair shone red in the sun. His eyes were as blue as the sky. The Chinese boy's dark eyes shone with excitement and joy. The two could not talk together, but they grinned. They started laughing and shouting all over again.

306

Then a procession formed back of the band. The two boys ran after it. They were no longer two strangers from two very different lands. Side by side they marched. They had both worked on the great transcontinental railroad. They were both Americans.

Abraham Lincoln did not live to see the railroad finished. He had been shot by a madman. Bitterly the country mourned his loss. But, as he had hoped, the new railway did help to unite the East and the West into one United States of America.

And so, little by little, our country changed from a land of covered wagons and homespun cloth and log cabins to a land of railways and factories and machinery. But it is not engines and factories that make a country great. There are no factories to make men like Washington and Lincoln. There are no machines to make children brave and strong and kind.

The people who live in a country make it great. A country is great if its people are brave and honest and unselfish. A country is great if its people can work together for the good of all.

Pioneer children from every land helped to make our country what it is. Children of today are just as important. They can help find new and better ways of doing things. They, too, can be pioneers.

BUILDING THE TRANSCONTINENTAL RAILROAD

1.

2.

First went the men to find the best route. They fought storms and Indians. They climbed mountains.

Next came the graders who made the roadbed smooth and even. They dug away hills. They filled in low places.

3.

4.

Wooden bridges or trestles were built over deep canyons. There were plenty of great pine trees in the forests.

Next came the men to lay the wooden ties for the tracks to rest upon. Around four million ties were needed.

5.

Last of all came the rail layers. The rails were brought up in a rail-truck. Four hundred rails to the mile.

6.

Down went a pair of rails. A man measured to see that they were the right distance apart.

7.

Then down swung the big hammers. Ten spikes to a rail. Three blows to a spike. Twelve thousand blows every mile.

8.

Sometimes Indians attacked the men while they were working. The men dropped their tools and picked up the guns they kept close by.

Word List

The following list tells where geographical and historical names, terms specially needed in a text of this sort, and slightly unusual words first appear. In a first history there are necessarily a number of such words. The teacher should use her discretion as to how much drill to give on any one word. Names of special interest in the child's locality should receive special attention. Names that are mentioned only once are starred. Place names should be located on a map to help children gain familiarity with new geographical names, but that is sufficient introduction. Names like Rocky Mountains, Mississippi River, etc., should receive more careful attention.

FIRST PIONEERS

2 pioneers
Asia
America
Atlantic
   Ocean

3 *Columbus
*Pinta
*Niña
*Santa María
Spain
Florida
steamships

radio
wrecked

4 Pedro
Catalina

5 spin
kettles
blankets

6 chest
New World
excited

7 sea gulls
shipwrecked
adventure
cannon
trumpets

8 bunks
bumped
bundle

9 complain
blazed
raisins

10 aboard
hymn

311

11 lanterns

12 Martin
chiefs

13 eagerly
alligators
dwarf
proudly
*Canary
Islands
weary
biscuit

14 dangerous
masts
tugged
thunder
boom

15 crashed
moaned

16 crazy
steered
groaned
creaked
leak
pump
mainmast

17 foam
bolt
splashed

crawled
slammed

18 precious
blade
bleeding

19 fierce
hammer
miserable
*Puerto Rico

20 carpenters
repairs
comet

21 palms
palmettos
general
Menéndez
armor
velvet
cape

22 knelt
warriors
ashore

23 St. Augustine
mainland
United States

24 Spanish
canvas
overboard

25 hold

ENGLISH PIONEERS

29 English
*Virginia

30 England
Jamestown
grumbled
Captain John
Smith

31 chopped
starving
runaway

32 knitting
overshoes

33 sidewalks
bucket
fireplace
ashes
gourd
shelf
grease
barrel
lye
homemade

34 housekeeper
linen
careless
borrowed

312

35 patch
mend
Ralph
squirrel
fluffy

36 scraped
cradle
napkins

37 famous
spun
woven

38 tickled
screens
tiptoe

39 protected
guard
strawberries

40 scratches
peered
rascal
grassy
juicy

42 fire hose
spark
bucketful

44 three-legged
thankful

45 cuddled
jacket

46 Pocahontas
captured
graceful

47 loft

48 dreaded

PILGRIM PIONEERS
FROM ENGLAND

53 Pilgrim
Plymouth

54 *Mayflower*
serious

55 split
beams
wooden pegs
cement mixers
brickyards
lumber yards
wedges
planks

56 Thomas
damp
searching

57 porcupine
frighten

58 strokes
fair-sized
gripped

59 helpless

60 firewood

61 bored

62 bleeding
willow
forked
sharpened

63 overboard
grunt
pluck

64 mess

65 forked
frame
teasing

313

66 extra
gasped
horror
jerk

68 splinters
thatched
reeds
grapevines
chimney

70 tenderly

71 beans
pumpkins
thanksgiving
feasting

73 latch

77 Holland

78 New York
City
New Amster-
dam
windmill

79 scrubbed
paddled
canoes
pastures

314

80 Peter
Trinka
Juliana

81 switched
tanks
stall

82 wolves
anxiously

83 lightning
squealing
bellow

84 galloping
cud
chew

86 buffaloes

87 moccasins
deerskin
dived
patience

88 scrambled

90 beaver
worried

91 poisoned

93 procession
skimmed
churned
Peter Stuyve-
sant

95 destroyed
*Duke of
York

96 dasher

97 lumps
buttermilk

102 France
French
St. Lawrence
explored
Mississippi
Great Lakes
birchbark

103 priests
Frenchman
Detroit
*Cadillac
factories
docks

315

150 Harris
*North Caro-
lina
Molly
John
Baby Susan
Jed

151 sheared
bleated

152 carded
tangles
yarn
spinning wheel
dye

153 loom
linen
linsey-
woolsey
shoemaker

154 fiddle

155 hickory bark
leather
raccoon
coon

157 upset
flint

160 shrill

163 crouched

164 owl
snarl

166 gleamed

167 stump

169 reel
stout

GOING WEST
BY WATER

174 flatboats

175 greedy
Ohio River

176 O'Neil
Joe
Betsy

177 *Boston
*Connecticut
sleigh
porridge
New York
State
stagecoach

178 Pennsylvania
oxcart
*Indiana
lilac bush

179 Mary Jane
Davy
headfirst
Martha
homespun
slits
bullets
quilts
pewter

180 Johnny Apple-
seed
judge

182 Old Dan
Tucker
toothache

186 pierce

188 slab
mattresses
hasty pudding
molasses

189 schoolhouse
schoolteacher

190 sampler

316

317

318